D0236596

contents

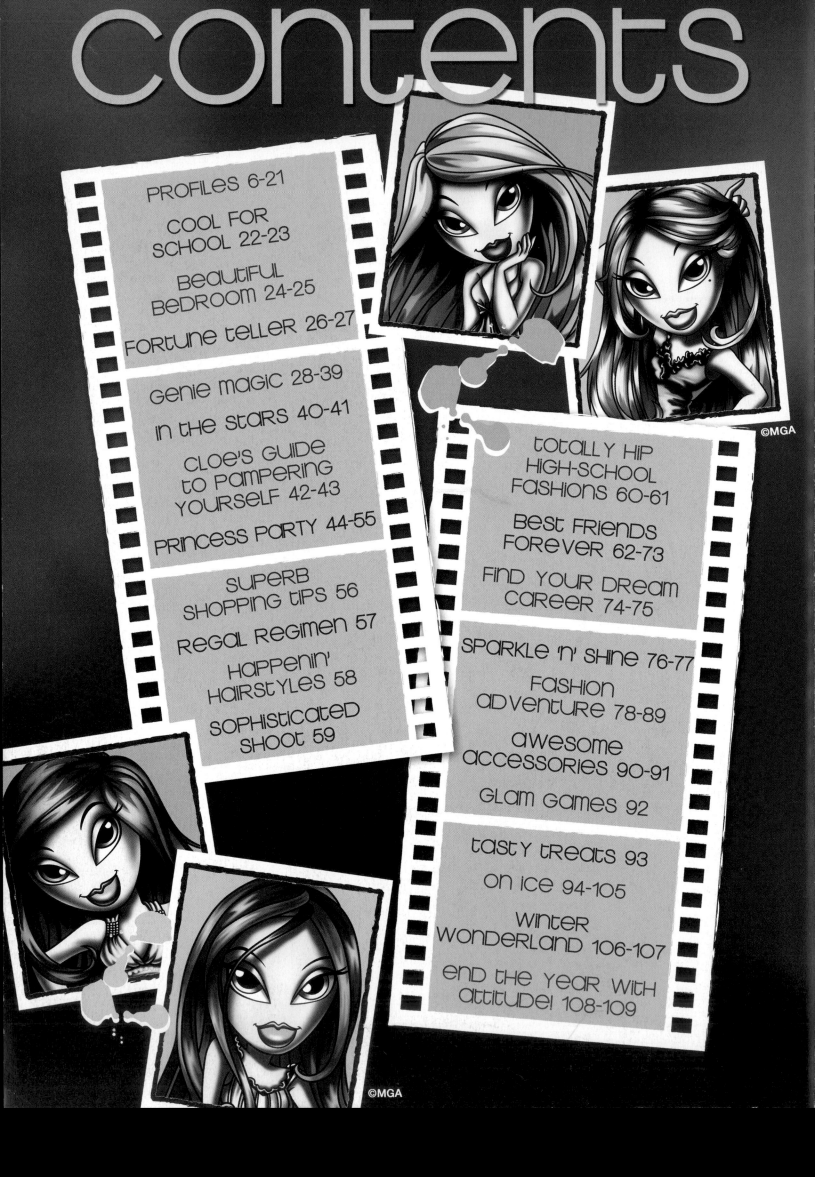

©MGA

©MGA

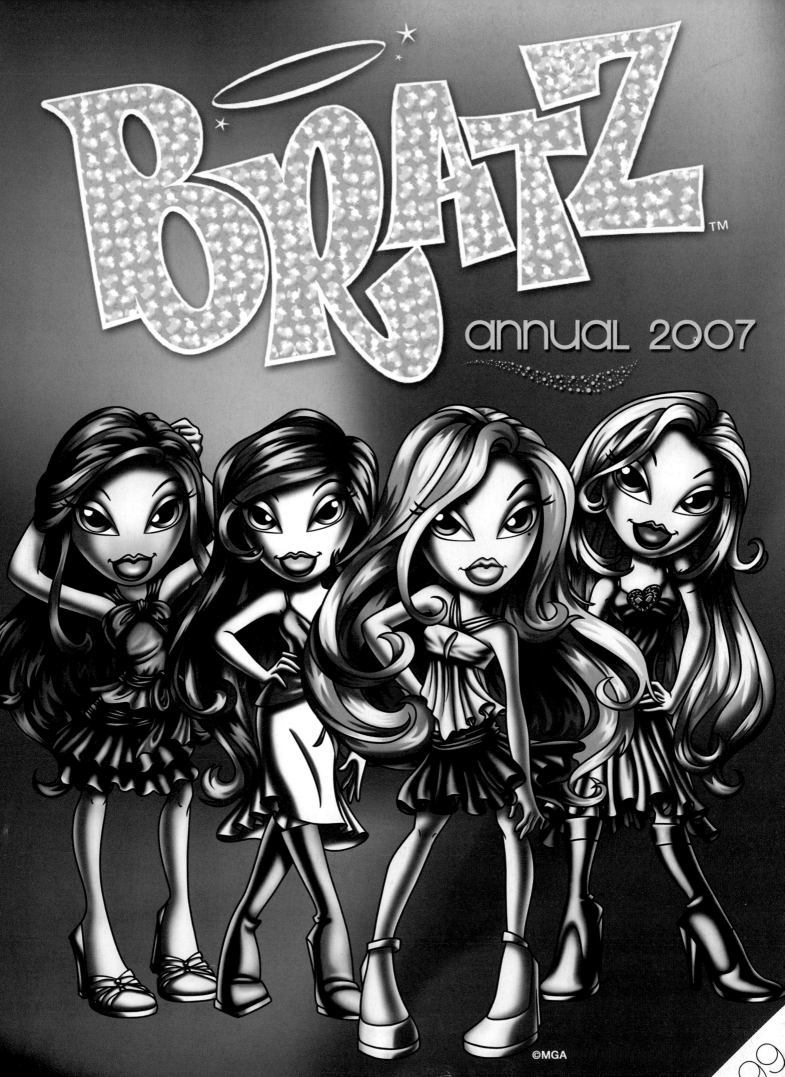

BRATZ™

annual 2007

©MGA

www.bratz.com
TM & © MGA Entertainment, Inc.
All Rights Reserved.
Used under license by Pedigree

Pedigree®

Published 2006
Published by Pedigree Books Limited,
Beech Hill House, Walnut Gardens, Exeter, Devon, EX4 4DH
Email: books@pedigreegroup.co.uk

£7.99

©MGA

Yasmin™

Quiet

My fave pastime is creative writing — and one day I'm gonna be a published author!

Down To Earth

Hi, I'm Yasmin (Pretty Princess to my friends!) and I can't wait to tell you all about the spectacular year we've had! I've been livin' it up and having a fabulous time with my friends; we're always ahead of the game with our fashions and our fun!

Check out page 94 to read about my icy adventure, and flip to my winter-wonderland tips on page 106.

(P.S. One rainy afternoon we had fun writing down words to describe each other — here are the words my friends wrote about me — as well as a few secret facts!)

Regal

My perfect day would be...visiting thrift markets with my friends and snagging some luxurious boho fashions, then kickin' back in a cosy armchair by the fire with a mug of hot chocolate and my fave book!

I'm lovin...spicy eastern foods – the tastes make me feel like I'm travelling the world!

Sweet

I like to step out in... graceful styles in autumn shades.

Creative

Sasha™
©MGA

Im lovin'... my dance class - it keeps my moves hip 'n' happenin'!

Hi, Im Sasha otherwise known as Bunny Boo! This year Ive been jammin' to some super-fine sounds and totally burnin' up the dance floor! Music is my biggest passion and I love nothin' better than checkin' out the hottest new bands with my best girls!

Try my quiz on page 74 to find your dream career - and on page 44 you can read about how we threw a totally royal bash! But first, here are some of my other passions - and the words my best girls use to describe me!

A note from Sa

Jade™

©MGA

Hi, I'm Jade! My friends call me Kool Kat because I've always got the inside track on the latest and greatest styles of the season! I love steppin' out in fashions and combinations that no one else is wearing. Whether I go for smooth and chic or retro cool, I always like to look runway ready!

You can read about the day we snagged tickets to an awesome fashion show on page 62. But first, here are a few Kool Kat secrets - and a few words my friends use to describe me!

Hip

My fave films are stylish European movies.

Unique

I'm lovin'...
girl-power popstars
- they make me
wanna hit the
dance floor!

Laid back

I like to step
out in... way-cool
new styles that
turn heads in
the street!

Cool

FASHION
FORWARD

My perfect day
would be... checkin' out
New York's vibe during fashion
week, hitting the trendiest
boutiques, then livin' it up
in New York's hot spots
with my best girls!

©MGA

Phoebe™

Hi, I'm Phoebe! I always try to be sensitive to what my friends are feeling - I think that's why they always come to me for advice!

You can call me: Sugar
Fave Smoothie: Orange
Fave Movies: Romances - I snuggle up on the sofa with chocs and a box of tissues to watch 'em!
Fave Food: Chocolate
Fave Music: Love Songs - I like music that touches my heart!
Shoppin' Style: Discovering boutiques and cute lil' shops and finding styles that no one else is wearing!

Hi, I'm Dana! I'm totally lovin' outer space, computers and science – sci-fi movies are my fave and I intend to open the first shoe shop in space! Talking of shoes... my huge collection of footwear inspired my friends to give me my nickname!

You can call me: Sugar Shoes

Fave Smoothie: Honeydew Melon – it always helps me chill after a major shoe shoppin' spree!

Fave Color: Purple

Fave Food: Chocolate chip cookies – homemade of course!

Fave Music: Classic blues

Best Body Part: Eyelashes – they were made for fluttering, girlfriend!

Dana™

©MGA

Maribel™ ©MGA

Hi, I'm Maribel! I love hot salsa music — but when I hit the ice, I'm totally chill! Ice skating is my passion and it's even more fun doing it with my friends!

You can call me: Party Penguin
Fave Food: Homemade tortillas
Fave Class: Does skate practice count as a class?
Best Body Part: I've gotta use my whole body to be a great skater!
Fashion Passion: Taking style off the street and adding a touch of cool glam.
Shoppin' Style: Online shopping — I don't have a lot of free time!

Hi, I'm Vinessa! My all-time fave thing is just hangin' out with a big group of friends – I'm almost never alone!

You can call me: Stylin' Sheep
Fave Colour: Silver
Fave Books: Poetry Books
Fave Class: Lunch is my fave part of the school day – cuz' I get to see my friends!
Best Body Part: Platinum blonde hair
Fashion Passion: Stylin' and restylin' my hair with cool accessories.

Vinessa
©MGA
™

Cloe ™

©MGA

I'm lovin'...giving my friends makeovers and inventing new cosmetic looks!

Hi, I'm Cloe! (My friends call me Angel, and I think it's a totally divine nickname!) Anyway, this has been a truly awesome year and we've been having loads of fun – and quite a few dramas along the way!

You can read all about our night of glitz and glamour on page 78 – and don't miss my guide to pampering yourself on page 42!

In the meantime, here are some of my faves – and some of the words my friends use to describe me!

My fave food is organic and vegetarian - cooking with fresh ingredients is as colourful and creative as designing new fashions!

Imaginative

I like to step out in...dramatic styles like animal-print fabrics and sparkling accessories - gotta make a splash!

Friendly

DRaMaTic

My perfect day would be... checkin' out the latest and greatest styles at the mall before heading for the beauty salon for a pampering session!

Glamorous

Siernna™

Hi, I'm Siernna and I'm a complete sports nut! I'm on almost every team so I'm always busy, but I always keep my cool – and that's why my friends call me Kool-ala!

Fave Colour: Blue

Fave Movies: Sports movies, duh!

Fave Books: Biographies of athletes – they help me to figure out my own goals!

Fave Music: Straight up rock 'n' roll gets me jumpin'!

Best Body Part: Strong, toned arms

Shoppin' Style: Finding stuff in sporting goods stores that's stylish enough to wear anywhere.

Hi, I'm Felicia!
I love the glam
life, but I love
the great
outdoors too.
I'm just as happy
dancin' at the hottest clubs as I am
pitchin' a tent in the woods!

You can call me: Glam Gecko

Fave Movies: Nature films – the natural
world is always interesting and totally
inspiring!

Fave Books: Nature photography books.

Fave Music: Anything I can dance to!

Fashion Passion: Layering different looks, so
I can change it up any time.

Shoppin' Style: Shopping a lot all at
one time, then going weeks or
months without buying a single
thing.

Felicia™

Cool for School!

If you want to expand your social life, there are tons of cool school activities that you can get involved in. Whether you're an outgoing cheerleader or a quiet writer, all you have to do is check out what's available at your school and find your perfect pastime!

School Yearbook

Does your school produce a yearbook at the end of each school year? There are sure to be plenty of ways to be part of it, from snapping pics of your classmates to jotting down the funniest things that happened through the year! It's a huge job and the more people who get involved, the more fun you'll have!

School Newspaper/Magazine

There are lots of different jobs available on the school magazine!

Journalist – Have you got a way with words? Find out if the school magazine needs any writers! You'll need to have an ear for a story and be able to write to a deadline!

Photographer – Every good magazine needs a good photographer! Make sure you've always got your camera with you – ready to grab those unexpected scoops!

Editor – if you're good at organising, this is the job for you! You've got to make sure all the pictures and stories are ready on time, and decide how they're all gonna work together!

Cheerleading

If you're sassy, loud and bursting with energy, why not try out for the cheerleading team at school? It's a super-fun way to work out while showing off your school spirit. You'll make great friends with all the school teams – and you'll get to wear some truly sizzlin' styles!

School Play

If you're a bit of a drama queen, maybe the school stage is the place for you. Check out the drama club and find out when the next auditions are going to be held. This could be your first step on the way to Hollywood!

Student Council

If you are interested in getting involved with the way your school is run, you could run for student council. This is a great way to really be a part of your school and have a say in what happens there!

Sports Team

If you love sport, you could try out for one of the school teams. You'll make some fantastic friends and you'll get to meet all sorts of other teams when you enter competitions. Not only will you have fun, but you'll also keep fit and healthy — and have fun at the same time!

Environmental Awareness Club

Are you the outdoors type, but don't wanna get sporty? Why not think about improving your school's green spaces? You could campaign to build a nature trail, create a pond or make a beautiful space where you and your friends can chill out in between classes!

Show Some Attitude!

Don't be put off if your school doesn't do something you'd like to try. If there isn't a drama club — create one! If your school has never produced a newspaper, start a trend, girl!

- Check with your teacher if they would be happy for you to go ahead with your idea.

- Ask if there are any school funds available to help you out.

- Find out whether there is a room you can use.

- Ask your best friends if they will help you get organised (if your friends are anything like Sasha, they're sure to say yes!). Come with a plan for how your club should work — what you want to do, how often to meet, etc.

- Tell everyone about your idea using posters and flyers.

- Ask everyone who is interested to add their name to a list. Then set a date for your first meeting and get goin'!

©MGA

Beautiful

Your bedroom isn't just a place to sleep - it's a super-important venue for everything from makeovers to sleepovers! So you've gotta make sure that it's as sweet and inviting as it can be. Here are some tips to turn your bedroom into a totally comfy, utterly sweet lounge where you and your girls will love hanging out!

Dressing Table

Use pretty pots to keep your nail files, eye pencils and makeup brushes tidy. Keep your mirror clean and make sure you have a really strong light. You could use small baskets to keep all your makeup together.

Sweet smelling fresh flowers

Always have a vase of fresh flowers in your room — they will smell and look super-sweet!

Cool Curtains

Drape colourful voile over your window or use a coloured blind instead of curtains to brighten up your room.

Fabulous Fashion Mags

Scatter your fave fashion mags on a couple of little tables so you and your friends will have something to flick through!

Space-saving Sofa

If you don't have much space, how about getting a fold-up sofa bed? In the daytime you can cover it with throws and comfy cushions, to make a great place to chat, read or design!

Cosy Toes

Look out for thick rugs that your bare feet will really sink into — think beauty and luxury, girl!

Bedroom

Music

Keep a stack of CDs by your stereo so you've got the right vibe for your mood. Fill out this list with your top CDs for every occasion!

SLEEPOVER MUSIC	
GIRLS' NIGHT OUT MUSIC	
MAKEOVER MUSIC	
DESIGNING AND DRAWING MUSIC	
CLEANING AND TIDYING MUSIC	
WRITING MUSIC	
GOSSIP-FEST MUSIC	
PARTY MUSIC	
GETTING READY FOR THE PROM MUSIC	
CHILL-OUT MUSIC	

Keep it Clean

Always put your clothes away — have a tidy wardrobe and chest of drawers. You don't want your girls to have to hunt for the chairs under piles of clothes!

Staying Cool

If your birthday's coming up, why not ask for a mini cooler to put in your room? It's a great way to keep those delicious smoothies cold in the summer!

Telephone

Make sure you have a stylin' telephone in your room so that you can stay in touch with your best friends and find out when they're on their way over!

Luscious Lighting

Check out your local antiques market for beautiful lamps with unusual shades. Your room will be much cosier with two or three little lamps instead of one glaring overhead light.

Extra Seating

You never know when more guests are gonna arrive! Beanbags are great for loungin' on, and you can stash them under your bed when they're not needed.

Fortune Teller

Here's How

1. Grab your best friend and sit opposite each other with the book between you.
2. Each of you put one finger on the crystal ball.
3. Close your eyes and concentrate on your best friend for one minute.
4. Now read out the questions one by one. Ask your friend to think of the answers - but not to say them out loud!
5. As you ask each question, keep concentrating on your friend's thoughts. Write down the answer that comes into your mind.
6. When you have finished asking all the questions, ask your friend what she was thinking about. You score one point for each correct answer.

26

©MGA

Questions

1. Think of a colour.

....

2. Think of a number between 1 and 10.

....

3. Who are you crushing on?

....

4. Think about a member of your family.

....

5. If you could have one magic power, what would you choose?

....

6. Think of a city that you have visited.

....

7. Think of an item of clothing that you are wearing.

....

8. Think of a shape.

....

9. If you could swap places with a movie star for the day, who would you choose?

....

10. Think of a music style.

....

score

10 - Congratulations - you are totally super-psychic!
6-9 - Quite impressive! You might have the makings of a fortune teller!
1-5 - You're not psychic - that's just pure luck!

Genie Magic ™

Hi, my name's Katia, and my story is gonna blow your mind! The first thing you've gotta do is believe something impossible. i'm a genie. i know it sounds crazy – even my best friends didn't believe me when i first told them! it all started one rainy night in a briefing room on an oil tanker...

A woman called Zell was watching a bank of monitors, searching for someone who had escaped. Hovering behind her was a mad scientist called Kon. "How could you let this happen?" he asked. "My Project G is in jeopardy because of you! Everything I've worked for!"

I had escaped from the ship! When I arrived in Stilesville, I crept out of the rain into a lil' nightclub called Pinz. On stage, an awesome band called the Rock Angelz was rockin' out on their guitars (although I didn't know what guitars were then!). I saw a nice-looking boy watching the band and moved towards him, hoping I could make a friend in this strange town.

Up on stage, Jade was totally excited. Matt Rock, the teen film star, was in the audience! When she came off stage Matt Rock followed her and asked her out on a date!

28

©MGA

I followed the boy I had seen backstage. He was Bryce, a friend of the band, and he was helping them pack equipment away. I knocked into Sasha by accident.

"Oh!" I cried. "Please accept my apology! Did I break your..." I looked at the thing she was holding, "... your, uh, that thing?"

"My guitar?" said Sasha. "No worries. **Hey, wicked shoes, sistah!**"

I was confused. I didn't understand modern speech back then! At that moment I saw a bouncer heading my way and I left in a hurry.

The next day, Yasmin and Jade were glued to a Matt Rock film on TV, while Cloe lay on the floor, studying. It was still pouring with rain outside. When the news and weather came on, Jade sighed happily.

"Isn't Matt Rock the greatest actor?"

On TV, the weatherman started to give his forecast. The weather was acting super weird all over the world - everyone was getting really worried! Cloe was worried too - about her geography test. She had to get an A in the test or she would be in real trouble with her parents!

©MGA

29

Just then, Sasha walked in. "People! My dream is about to become reality!" she declared. "B-HIP Radio is auditioning teen DJs for a part-time gig! Sasha is about to take over the airwaves!"

Sasha's friends congratulated her. "Better take an umbrella," Yasmin said. "Seems like this rain is never going to let up. I feel so sorry for all those stray animals out there stuck in the rain. If I could, I'd build a deluxe pet shelter right here to help them."

"What's up with this wacky weather anyway?" asked Sasha.

In the briefing room, Kon and Zell were watching the weather on their monitors. "The deserts are turning to seas, the tropics to icebergs - everything is going according to my plan," Kon boasted. "Everyone has agreed to my demands."

Just then my father, Ali, walked in. Kon quickly hit a button and the monitors switched to views of pleasant weather.

"Have they found her?" asked Ali.

"We're doing everything we can," Kon replied.

The following day, I went to my very first day of high school, and ran into Yasmin, Sasha, Jade and Cloe again in the Stiles High cafeteria. They seemed really nice and I wanted to make friends with them - but suddenly I saw two thugs outside the window - and they were looking for me!

My new friends helped me hide, but when the thugs had gone they demanded an explanation. I explained that I lived at a government installation. My father and I were working on classified projects.

"All I want is two more days of freedom, a chance to see what it's like to be a real teenager," I said.

The girls invited me to go over to Cloe's for a girls' night and we had tons of fun - until we heard a noise downstairs! I thought it was the thugs, but it turned out to be two of the girls' friends - Dylan and Bryce, who was the nice boy I'd seen in the club!

Cloe was really cross. "Bryce, Dylan, how could you? You guys scared me to death! I wish you would totally croak!"

Oh no - it was a wish! I couldn't help but react! I tugged at my earring and the guys morphed into frogs!

After that, I couldn't hide the truth! We told the guys to wish themselves human again, and I granted their wish. Then, I explained about being a genie.

"My father was a genie," I explained, "but his bottle was broken long ago and he lost his powers."

©MGA

©MGA

"So you can grant wishes?" Cloe asked.

"For others only, and only one per person," I replied.

When Cloe realised that she had already used up her only wish, she was horrified. The others agreed to share their wishes with her, and I explained that that meant that any of them could make the last three wishes. They were totally psyched, but soon they started to argue.

"You guys, one wish has to be that Matt Rock is my new boyfriend," said Jade. "Think of all the hot parties and movie premieres we'll get to go to!"

"Fine," said Sasha, "just so I get to be B-HIP's new DJ. No way can I leave anything to chance with all the competition I'm up against."

"I'm cool with that, provided there's one left over for my deluxe pet shelter," said Yasmin.

"What about me?" Cloe cried. "I've got to get an A on my geography final! Without it I'll be grounded for life."

"Hey, while they're busy fighting over wishes, do you want to hang out some time?" Bryce asked me.

"Hang out?" I asked, not sure what he meant.

"He's asking you on a date," Dylan explained, grinning.

©MGA

My new friends helped me pick an outfit for my date with Bryce, and at first the date went well, but then I started to feel exhausted. I had been out of my bottle for too long and I was losing energy! Then I saw the thugs - they were still looking for me! I said goodbye to Bryce and raced out of the mall.

Outside, the girls were still arguing about what to wish for. They saw me run out of the mall. I knew I needed to get home, so I decided to get into the limo.

"Katia! Where are you going?" Cloe yelled.

"Don't be alarmed," I said, trying to remember the new words I'd learned. "I'm... cool. I'm going home to straighten things out with my father. But, let's... hang... later, kay?"

When my father saw me he was relieved that I was safe, but angry that I had run away. I tried to tell him about my wonderful new friends, but it was no use. He thought humans only wanted us for our magic, and I was sent to my room in disgrace.

©MGA

Back in Stilesville, Jade had a date with Matt Rock and Sasha was one of the final ten contestants in the DJ contest - and they'd both got what they wanted all on their own! They were all still bickering about the wishes, when Cloe cried "Real friends would let me have my wish!" The others were so hurt that Cloe wished she'd never said it, accidentally using up another wish! Now they only had two wishes left!

"Um, Bunny Boo," said Cloe. "Since you're sure to get the DJ job, can I-"

"No!" yelled Yasmin and Sasha together.

"Cloe, that's it!" said Yasmin. "I'm helping you cram for your test. You're going to ace it and I'm getting my pet shelter!"

Back on the ship, I overheard Kon and Zell in the briefing room - and they were talking about my new friends!

"You'll interrogate Katia's friends and, if they know about her powers, eliminate them," I heard Kon say. I gasped. I had to do something!

I rushed to my father's study. "Father, Kon and Zell have been using us!" I cried. "I have to go warn my friends! Kon and Zell want to hurt them and-"

"Not another word!" he roared. "I can't believe you would resort to making up lies about Kon and Zell, who have done nothing but protect you! GO TO YOUR ROOM!"

©MGA

I raced to my room, grabbed my rolled carpet and rucksack and escaped – I was going back to Stilesville to warn my friends! But I was already too late. Yasmin was helping Cloe cram for her Geography test when all the lights went out. They thought it was Dylan and Bryce playing tricks again – until they opened the door and saw the thugs looking down at them!

I raced back to Stilesville on my flying carpet and found Bryce. As soon as I told him what was going on, he called Jade and arranged to meet at the B-HIP radio station, where Sasha was doing her final audition.

Soon we were all standing outside the radio station in the pouring rain. "I'm sorry you had to rush your audition," Sasha," I said.

"Forget about it," she replied. "My girlfriends come first. Man, I wish I'd brought my umbrella."

BAM! An umbrella appeared in her hand. She had blown a wish – and I couldn't take it back for her!

When we reached Cloe's house, the door was wide open and the house was dark. We went inside, but the place was empty. I was devastated – I knew where they had been taken!

©MGA

Then someone Jade and Sasha knew walked into the room. Jade gasped. "Byron! Katia and Bryce, this is Byron. He produces reality TV shows."

"I'm also a secret agent," Byron explained. "Reality TV makes a great cover!"

Byron told me that Kon and Zell were not with the Earth Safety Association. Kon was the founder of the ESA - the Evil Scientists Association! He had been using me to create worldwide havoc by disrupting weather patterns.

"They said I was helping people!" I cried.

"Why are they doing this?" I asked.

"So Kon can force governments to pay him to stop the destruction. Once every major country is penniless and, as a result, powerless, he will take over the world."

Byron told Jade and Sasha that they had to keep me hidden while he and his team rescued Cloe, Yasmin and my father. "Do you still have your spy equipment?" he asked. Jade and Sasha held up their lipstick and compacts. When Byron was gone, I persuaded the others that I had to go help him!

In the briefing room, my father saw all the terrible weather on the monitors! "Didn't Katia help you with your project to control the weather and make the Earth safe?" he cried. Suddenly Father saw Kon and Zell in a new light. He decided to leave and find me!

©MGA

36

When my father had gone into his room, Zell fiddled with the wires in a control panel next to his study door. Next time my father entered his study, the door would lock and the thermostat would drop to freezing!

Just as my father arrived in Stilesville, I was showing Jade, Bryce and Sasha how to ride a magic carpet.
"It's just like skateboarding," I said. "It's all about balance!"
We took off - heading for the lab!

In the lab, Yasmin and Cloe had been given truth serum! They couldn't stop themselves telling Kon and Zell everything! When Kon had found out who else knew about my magic powers, he told his goons to give the girls a mind sweep - he was going to turn them into brainless assistants!

When we arrived at the lab, we split up. While I was looking for my father, Jade and Sasha were trapped by Kon! But they still had the equipment Byron had given them. They fired beams from their lipsticks, knocking two thugs out. Then they flashed their compacts at Kon's eyes, temporarily blinding him with light beams!
Zell had strapped Yasmin and Cloe into huge machines, but Bryce and I arrived just in time to save them from the mind sweep. Zell escaped as we were rescuing our friends.

©MGA

Jade and Sasha soon found us, but so did Kon! He was holding up my bottle.

"Freeze, or I'll smash this into a thousand pieces!" he said.

"Tell me where my father is!" I cried.

But Kon didn't know. Then my friends said that I could use the one wish they had left to find my father.

"We wish Katia's father was back in his study!" said Yasmin.

I smiled at her gratefully and tugged my ear. Now my father was safe!

But then Kon started to laugh. "You stupid, silly girls. Do you know what you've done? Ali's lab is rigged to lock and deep freeze him!"

He hit a button and a picture came onto a monitor. Father was shivering madly in his lab, icicles forming on his chin!

"You monster!" I cried.

"Watch yourself, Missy," Kon snarled. "Remember, Katia, the only reason people like you is because you can grant their wishes."

"That is so not true!" yelled Sasha.

My friends jumped Kon and wrestled the bottle from him. But my father was stiff and icy. In a flash, I knew what I had to do. "I have to break my bottle," I said. All the wishes I had granted would be reversed. But I would lose my powers too...

©MGA

38

I smashed my bottle on the ground and it shattered into a million pieces.

Sasha's umbrella disappeared. All the terrible weather went into reverse. And my father popped back outside his study, alive and well.

"Katia, we are so proud of you," said Yasmin.

"Congratulations!" said Jade. "You got your wish! You're just a normal teenager now."

In the briefing room, Zell set the ship to self destruct - in five minutes! Byron tried to stop her, but Kon walked in behind them and knocked Byron out cold. Zell double-crossed Kon and handcuffed him to Byron - then left!

Byron figured out the cancellation code for the self-destruct program just in time... and then my father walked in.

"Katia," he said, "I want you to be happy, and I'll do whatever it takes. We'll move close to your friends and the school, and finally have a normal life."

"That's all I ever wanted!" I cried.

Kon was arrested, all the money was given back and I started a new life in Stilesville! Byron got his network to donate money for Yasmin's pet shelter. Cloe got her A and Sasha won the DJ competition. Jade found out that Matt Rock waxed his legs and had to dump him.

But best of all, I got to lead a normal life - with the best friends anyone could ever have!

39

©MGA

In the Stars

Check out your stars for the year ahead!

Aries
21 March – 20 April

Fashion: Check out bright and bold colours this season – with your inner confidence you can carry anything off!

Friends: Beware of new friends who make promises they can't keep. Stay loyal to your old buds – they'll never let you down!

Life: This is gonna be a challenging year for you – full of ups and downs. But hang in there girl, 'cuz there are some awesome rewards heading your way!

Taurus
21 April – 21 May

Fashion: Go for earthy colours – chocolate browns, forest greens and autumn reds!

Friends: You're an incredibly loyal friend and you know how important it is to value your best girls. Make sure you organise plenty of sleepovers and girls' nights out this year!

Life: This is the year you really need to work hard at school. Get down with your books and your hard work will totally pay off!

Gemini
22 May – 21 June

Fashion: Go for versatile separates that give you tons of different outfits!

Friends: Your friends will need you as much as you need them this year. But watch out for a friend who likes to put you down – that's not real friendship!

Life: This year is gonna be full of changes for you, so sit back, stay cool and enjoy the ride!

Cancer
22 June – 23 July

Fashion: Concentrate on the natural colours of the sea – blue, turquoise and green (but don't forget those bright coral reefs too!)

Friends: This is a great year for making friends – whether they're boys or girls! Don't let yourself worry or feel insecure – just count up all the great friends you've got and remember they love you for who you are!

Life: You don't mind a bit of hard work, and soon you're gonna see the rewards. It's a great year for you!

Leo
24 July – 23 August

Fashion: You're a showstopper and you should wear fashions that reflect that! The more outrageous the better – use Jade as your fashion inspiration!

Friends: You are a fantastic friend and you'll always be there for your best girls – but make sure you listen to what they say and don't always try to be the leader of the pack!

Life: This is your year to shine, girl! Lots of opportunities are heading your way – you just have to look out for them!

Virgo
24 August – 23 September

Fashion: Classic styles are gonna be your best buys this year. It's worth spending a little bit extra on the high street for those well-cut looks that never go out of fashion!

Friends: You're fun to be with and an awesome friend – you'll find your best girls coming to you often for advice and words of wisdom this year!

Life: You have tons of ambition and you like to have clear goals in view – if you focus on your dreams this year, you'll move a long way towards them coming true!

Libra
24 September - 23 October

Fashion: White is the hottest shade in fashion this year! For a look that oozes style, team wide legged white linen trousers with a knee-length fitted shirt and a long necklace.

Friends: You like to balance your time between friends and family – but be careful that this year none of your friends end up feeling left out!

Life: This is a great year to try something new. Why not start dance lessons or join a drama club?

Scorpio
24 October - 22 November

Fashion: Choose combat trousers, cute lil' tees and soft zip-up tops for a chilled-out sporty look.

Friends: You are a great friend but a scary enemy! Don't be too hard on your friends when they make mistakes. It happens to everyone – even you!

Life: This year is going to be full of drama and excitement for you – sometimes it will seem as if you haven't got any time to relax! Make sure you put aside some regular time to unwind with a book or a good film.

Sagittarius
23 November - 22 December

Fashion: You should wear bright, jewel colours and layer your clothes for a fresh, modern look.

Friends: Make sure you know who your real friends are – someone will try to take advantage of your generosity this year.

Life: Your next holiday will have some great surprises in store. Make sure you're prepared for anything and take plenty of snaps to show your best girls!

Capricorn
23 December - 20 January

Fashion: This is the year to concentrate on your shoe and boot collection. Make sure you have the right footwear for any occasion!

Friends: Sometimes you feel a bit scared of telling people how you really feel – even your best friends. But you can trust them, so don't be afraid to let go of a few secrets sometimes!

Life: You know what you want out of life and you are pretty determined to get it! Keep working towards your goals and aim high!

Aquarius
21 January - 19 Febuary

Fashion: This year, experiment with some completely new styles. The best styles are all about finding fashions that work for you, so try everything from punk to princess!

Friends: You love making friends and meeting new people – this year you're gonna meet a friend you will know for the rest of your life!

Life: Do you believe in magic? 'Cuz this is gonna be a totally magical year for you, girl!

Pisces
20 Febuary - 20 March

Fashion: Look out for fresh, floaty fashions in pastel colours to create a feminine, charming style.

Friends: You may not have a huge group of friends, but just one great friend is more than enough – and you will be friends forever!

Life: This is going to be a happy year for you – you'll have loads of fun and maybe even a little bit of romance!

©MGA

Whether you're tired, blue or just in need of a lil' TLC, check out my fave ways to relax!

Cloes' Guide to

Blissful Bath

Fluffy towels • Luxuriously soft dressing gown • Stylin' slippers • Aromatherapy bath oil • Scented candles (make sure you OK this with your 'rents though!)

1. Fill a bath with hot water and relaxing aromatherapy bath oil.

2. Light scented candles and place them around the bathroom.

3. Put a fluffy bath sheet next to the bath ready to wrap yourself in!

4. Lock the door and hang a 'Do Not Disturb' sign on the handle — this is your relaxation time!

5. After your bath, rub moisturiser into your skin and slip into your dressing gown and slippers, before curling up with a fave book or movie!

Magical Manicure

Nail-varnish-remover pads • Nail file • Bowl of warm water • Scented oil • Nail scissors • Hairdryer • Base-coat nail varnish • Nail varnish in your chosen colour • Sealant

1. First, remove any old nail varnish. Use a nail-varnish-remover pad and wipe it across the surface of your nail until all the old varnish has gone.

2. Give your hands and nails a thorough wash, using plenty of soap.

3. Dry your hands. Now it's time to decide on a shape for your nails! Long nails look amazing, but they can be really hard to maintain — especially if you're into playing sports! I always try to keep my nail length just a couple of millimetres beyond the tip of my finger. This cuts down on nail breakage and looks fabulous, without getting in the way of your activities!

4. Your nail shape should suit the shape of your hands and fingers. Remember:

Slim, elegant fingers suit almond-shaped nails.

Wider hands and fingers suit squared-off ends.

If you're not sure, make the shape of your nails the same as the shape of your cuticles.

5. Use your emery board to make the shape you want. You should only use the emery board in a single direction, starting at the edge and working along the nail towards the centre. Never file too deeply into the corners.

6. Next, soak your nails in a bowl of warm water. Add some scented oil to the water to make your hands super soft.

7. Keep your hands in the water until they just start to wrinkle. Then use a soft towel to pat them dry. When they are completely dry, lightly buff them with an extra-fine buffer.

8. Apply a thin layer of base coat and allow it to dry just until your nails are tacky. Now apply a very thin layer of colour. It should only take three or four strokes to cover the nail. Don't worry if you can see the brush marks on the nail. You won't see them when the polish dries.

9. When the coloured varnish is completely dry, apply another thin coat. Repeat this until you have three very thin layers.

10. When your coloured nail varnish has dried, apply a sealant. This will protect your nails from chipping. You can re-apply this sealant every two or three days

Pampering yourself

Backflip

When you have done a few basic manicures, you can try the backflip manicure! Before you start, you need to choose two nail-varnish colours. You can pick colours that go together well, or go for a really unexpected combo – the choice is yours!

1. When you are ready to apply the base coat, put it on underneath your nail as well as on top of the nail.

2. Apply your main colour to the top of your nail, just as you would for the normal manicure.

3. When the thin layers are dry, turn your hands over and apply the second colour underneath. Apply three very thin layers.

4. When everything is dry, apply the sealant on both sides of the nail. Everyone will be asking how you got your dazzlin' nail style

Perfect Pedicure

1. Fill a wide bowl with hot water and add a handful of Epsom salts.

2. Use a nail-varnish-remover pad to remove any old colour from your nails.

3. Clip your toenails straight across.

4. Use an emery board to file your nails, rounding them at the corners.

5. Soak your feet in hot water for five minutes, then dip an emery footfile into the water and use it to smooth all the rough areas of your feet.

6. Pat your feet dry, making sure that you dry in between each toe.

7. Massage both feet with moisturising lotion.

8. Separate your toes with a foam separator.

9. Wipe any excess moisturiser off your nails. Then apply one thin layer of base coat and three thin layers of colour.

10. Finish with a coat of sealant to perfect your look!

Cloe's Top Tip

When you have mastered manis and pedis, why not throw a Pamper Party? Use soothing aromatherapy oils to create a totally chilled-out vibe and spend the day treating yourselves! You could end the day by giving each other makeovers and stylin' new hairdos – perfect for an awesome girls' night out!

©MGA

43

Hi, i'm Jade, and i've got a royally exciting story to tell you! it all started when we were chilling at our fave café in the mall...

"I can't believe it's the end of summer already!" I groaned.
"It's been an awesome holiday, though," said Yasmin, sipping a glass of cranberry juice. "We've all done amazing things!"
"I saw some fabulous fashions in New York," I agreed, thinking about my trip to the city.
"I loved catching the rays on a tropical beach!" Sasha added with a smile.

"But Cloe's holiday was the best," said Phoebe.
"Travelling around Europe - you must have seen some fantastic places!"
Cloe flashed a wide, happy smile. "It was unbelievable," she admitted.
"What was the best thing about it?" I asked, thinking she'd talk about the art in Florence or the street styles in Milan. But she totally surprised me!

"It's gotta be the castles," she said dreamily. "You guys, there were castles everywhere! They were just like something out of a fairytale! They had spires and turrets - and they were high up on top of green hills - spectacular!"
"Sounds amazing," Yasmin sighed.

©MGA

©MGA

"Can you imagine how wonderful it would be to be a real princess?" Cloe went on with shining eyes. "To live in castles like that, just like in the old days?"

"Sorry to burst your bubble, Angel," I said, flicking my eyebrow up. "But old-fashioned princesses had a ton of rules to follow... who they could date, what they could wear, what they could do..."

"That doesn't sound like much fun," said Sasha, wrinkling her nose.

"OK," Cloe agreed, "then I'll be a modern-day princess! I'll be just as glam and I'll still get to live in the fairytale castle - but I'll be totally independent and make all my own rules!"

"Perfect!" Yasmin exclaimed. "That's what modern-day princesses should be about - never bowing to the pressure!"

"We're all princesses on the inside!" Sasha added. "If only princesses didn't have to go back to school," I sighed.

"Cheer up!" said Yasmin. "We always have tons of fun at school - and we'll all be together - that's the main thing!"

"I know what Kool Kat means, though," said Cloe. "School's great, but I'm bummed that this awesome summer has to end!"

"You guys, we should have a major party before heading back to school!" said Sasha.

"Yeah!" cried Phoebe, picking up on the idea in a flash. "We need to end this spectacular summer in style!"

"But it would have to be a truly magnificent party," said Cloe. "Something that would top every other end-of-summer party we've been to!"

"Something that would be remembered for years to come!" Yasmin added.

I was thinking hard - inspiration had hit and my imagination was buzzing!

"How about a princess-themed party?" I said. "Cloe's princess fixation might not be such a fairytale after all!"

Cloe jumped up in excitement and nearly spilled her drink - Yasmin grabbed it just in time!

"That's a superb idea!" Cloe squealed. "We could design some regal invitations on really posh-looking paper!"

"And decorate the venue like a palace ballroom!" Sasha added.

"We'll tell everyone that it's a princess theme so we'll all look like royalty!" said Phoebe.

"Tiaras and jewels and pearls and lace!" Yasmin cried in excitement.

"This is the hottest idea we've ever had!" Cloe said, beaming.

"But what about the venue?" asked practical Sasha. "We can't just hold this party at someone's pad - it's gotta be somewhere magnificent!"

46

©MGA

"Just like those castles in Europe!" breathed Cloe.

"We're not going to hold this party in Europe, Angel," I said with a smile. "But leave it with me... I've got an idea."

I told my best girls that I'd catch up with them later and headed over to the cinema, which was owned by a really cool businesswoman called Elly. We had helped her out when her cinema opened by handing out leaflets and telling all our friends about it, and after that she had said she owed us a favour!

"You bought the old ballroom, didn't you?" I asked. "The place where they used to hold dances in the old days?"

"That's right," said Elly. "It's been empty for years but it's a gorgeous old building, so I thought I would restore it and turn it into a romantic hot spot! I'm calling it the Crystal Ballroom. It's all finished now and it's opening to the public in two weeks."

I explained our idea about a magnificent end-of-summer ball.

"So you want to throw this spectacular party in the Crystal Ballroom?" Elly asked. I nodded and Elly gave me a huge smile. "It's yours!" she said.

©MGA

The others were totally bowled over when they found out that I had snagged the Crystal Ballroom for the party! We went over there straight away to check it out and decide how we were gonna decorate.

Elly had done a fabulous job restoring the old building - it looked high class and we could tell it was gonna be a dazzlin' hot spot. There were crystal chandeliers hanging from the high ceiling, gold brocade upholstery on couches around the edge of the room and fleur-de-lys wallpaper that made me think of the French kings and queens I'd read about in History!

We grabbed all the society magazines we could find to check out what kinds of parties today's young heirs were throwing. I decided to go lavish and think big! We draped swags of rich, cream-coloured material around the walls and trailed glitzy strings of beads from the chandeliers to add extra sparkle!

We sprinkled coloured gems on every table and hung gilt-framed mirrors on the walls - they would make the room look even bigger and reflect all the gorgeous outfits our friends would be wearing!

"This party is gonna be way glam!" said Yasmin as she finished placing vases of lilies around the room. "What's next?"

48

©MGA

"Invitations!" said Cloe firmly. "A party this posh has gotta be invitation only!"

"It's just like a fairytale!" said Phoebe. "We're gonna invite every eligible prince and princess we know!"

We used thick, creamy card to make the invitations and Cloe designed a regal look, which we all copied using silver and gold pens. Soon we had a towering pile of invitations to give out to all our friends! We enlisted some of our guy friends to help us deliver them and everyone said they would come!

"This is gonna be an awesome party, ladies," said Cameron, when all the invitations had been delivered.

"Totally," I agreed. "But it would be even more awesome if we had a totally fabulous sound system!"

Cameron grinned at me. "You mean, a sound system like the one Dylan has?"

"Hey, that's an inspired suggestion, Blaze!" I said, opening my eyes wide.

"Do you think Fox'll lend it to us?" asked Sasha.

"I hope so," said Cloe anxiously, "what's a party without music?"

"No worries," said Cameron, smiling at Cloe. "We'll set it up for you too - and we'll make sure there are some royally cool tracks to dance to!"

©MGA

"Just one thing left to do," I said, pushing back my hair. "My fave thing!"
"Shopping!" everyone said at once. We needed some fabulous new outfits to show off at the party of the year!

We hit the mall and spent an amazin' few hours picking out glam new looks - I was super-inspired by the princess theme and I knew exactly what kind of look I was aiming for. We picked out frilly skirts and paired them with totally hot tank tops, glittering with studs and diamantes! I spotted a superb pair of tight cuffed jeans with a studded pattern across the back that would pick up on the jewellery I wanted to wear.

Phoebe's outfit was awesome - a peacock-blue skirt with tons of netting so it stood out around her in true princess style! Sasha picked out a faux-fur shrug-style jacket that would make any outfit look totally luxurious, and Yasmin found a fashion-forward bodice studded with diamantes. Cloe definitely looked the part of a modern-day princess in a low-waisted tiered skirt and a glittering top. We finished up the day in our fave accessories shop, where we picked out chandelier earrings and tiaras!

©MGA

On the night of the party, we all met up early at Cloe's house. Cloe gave us manicures and painted tiny tiaras on our fingernails. We carefully styled our hair and placed our tiaras on top of our finished dos, securing them with tiny grips so they didn't come off while we were groovin' on the dance floor!

We spent a long time making sure that our make-up was just right - modern-day princesses should always look flawless and finished! Then we got into our outfits and checked ourselves out in the mirror.

"Utterly regal!" pronounced Sasha.

"I really do feel like royalty!" Cloe exclaimed, doing a little pirouette. We were all struttin' superior style and I knew that we were gonna have a blast at the party - I couldn't wait to get there! We were about to call a taxi when we heard a horn beeping outside.

It was Cameron - and he was driving a white Cadillac! We rushed outside, gasping and giggling. Cameron stepped out of the car and opened the doors for us.

"I thought that real-life princesses deserved a real-life knight on a white steed", he joked.

"Except this ride is way easier on our hairdos!" I added as we climbed in.

©MGA

When the Cadillac pulled up at the Crystal Ballroom, the party was already hoppin'. Cameron and Dylan had done a great job setting up the sound system, which was blasting out the latest and greatest tunes! We walked into the party and tons of people came up to tell us what an awesome venue we'd picked. I stopped to chat to Fianna and Meygan, while Yasmin and Sasha headed straight for the dance floor!

Soon Bunny Boo and Pretty Princess were bustin' out some hot dance moves - you could tell that they were having great fun and they looked super cool! In fact, they looked so cool that Dylan wanted to get in on the scene!
"How hard can it be?" he said, moving over to join them.

Big mistake!

The Fox has got some slick moves - but he is nowhere near as coordinated as Sasha and Yasmin! He tried to imitate them but he lost control of his feet and skidded sideways... slamming right into the sound system he'd set up!

©MGA

There was a horrible screeching, whining sound and the music stopped as the speakers toppled to the floor. A cry went up from everyone at the party.

"Well done, Fox," said Cameron sarcastically. He pulled Dylan from the wreckage and shook his head. "When are you gonna learn - you'll never have moves as slick as these girls'!"

"Dude, what happened?" asked Eitan, strolling over to us. Poor Dylan just shook his head.

I was trying not to show how upset I was feeling, but Cloe launched into full drama queen mode.

"This is a disaster!" she cried. "What's a party without music? This was supposed to be the most amazing party ever - the party people would remember forever!"

"It still will be," said Sasha calmly. "Chill out, Angel."

"It'll be remembered for being the most disastrous party ever!" Cloe went on, almost in tears. Cameron glared at Dylan.

"That's not what I mean," said Sasha. "You guys, we can fix this! We already look like pop princesses - why don't we bust out our guitars and jam?"

We all stared at her for a moment, then I smiled. "Bunny Boo, sometimes you are a complete genius!" I said. "Let's do it!"

©MGA

53

Cameron, our knight in shining armour, sped off in the white Cadillac to fetch our guitars and amp. While he was gone we set up a stage at one end of the ballroom and as soon as Blaze returned, we were in position.

Sasha grabbed the mic as we tuned our guitars.
"You guys, welcome to the Crystal Ballroom!" she called. There was a huge cheer. "It's the end of a fabulous summer and we're gonna celebrate in royal style - 'cuz we're the pop princesses that are gonna rock this ballroom!"
There was an even louder cheer than before, and we started our first song, putting all our energy into the performance. This had to work!

Our songs sounded so fabulous that soon all our friends were on the dance floor. In fact, there were way more people dancing than there had been before!
"Can you believe this?" I asked Yasmin as Sasha launched into a solo riff.
"It's amazing!" Yasmin agreed. "Just don't let Dylan dance anywhere near our guitars, OK?"

©MGA

The party was by the far the biggest, best and most regal end-of-summer event we could remember, and we knew it would be talked about every summer for years to come! Our friends danced all night and everyone had a spectacular time. The décor looked amazing and the mirrors made it seems like there were twice as many people there!

After the last guests had gone and we had tidied the venue up, we headed back to Sasha's pad, tired and happy.

"I think we should try being modern-day princesses more often," Cloe said with a wide yawn.

"I don't mind going back to school now," I said, snuggling down into my sleeping bag.

"Everyone's gonna be talking about the party of the year!"

"Totally," agreed Sasha, flicking out the light. "It was the perfect end to the perfect summer!"

"We are the ruling pop princesses," said Yasmin in the dark. "And Jade is definitely the reigning queen of party planning!"

©MGA

Superb Shopping Tips

There is definitely an art to shopping - if you get it wrong you can end up trudging around the mall with sore feet and buyer's remorse! Check out our hottest tips to make sure that you'll be the queen of the mall!

👑 Know exactly what you want to buy and how much you can spend - and stick to it! Tell your best friends what your budget is - they can help keep you in line.

👑 Don't buy something just because it's a bargain! If you won't wear it, it's still not a good deal!

👑 If you are looking for something to complete an outfit, take the rest of the outfit with you. Then you can try it all on together to check out how it looks!

👑 Buy styles that suit your shape and colouring.

👑 If you see something in a magazine that you totally dig, find out your nearest stockist (most mags have a list of stockists in the back, or list them next to the pics of the items). If there isn't a branch near you, many clothing shops now have websites so you can order online.

👑 Never settle for a less-than-perfect fit.

👑 Shop with friends who you know will be totally honest with you. Some people will tell you that anything looks great because they're afraid of hurting your feelings, but that way you will end up with a wardrobe full of mistakes!

👑 Take plenty of breaks for smoothies, snacks and chats and you won't lose that shopping buzz!

👑 Cut pics out of fashion mags of clothes you really like and keep them in your handbag. You'll have great fun looking for the exact item - and you might find a bargain version if you're lucky!

👑 Never go shopping when you're in a rush - you'll grab something random just because you're panicking!

👑 Always wear slip-on shoes so you can kick them off easily in the changing room. Wear clothes that aren't too fiddly to take on and off - a dress that pulls on over your head with no zips or buttons is ideal.

👑 Sign up to the email or mailing list of your fave shops. You'll be the first to hear about sales and you might even get some discount vouchers!

👑 If you're not sure about something, wait 24 hours. If you wake up the next morning wishing you had it, then you know it's not an impulse buy!

©MGA

Regal Regimen

It's time to start looking after your skin. Treat it like royalty and you'll soon be glowing like a princess!

Step 1

Cleanse your skin every morning and evening.

Choose a light cleanser that will keep your pores clean and be gentle on your skin. Be especially careful if you have sensitive skin, and test any new products before using them on your face.

Take a cotton wool pad and splash a few drops of cleanser onto it.

Then wipe the pad all over your face and neck in long, firm strokes. You'll see the dirt being wiped away to reveal your true gorgeousness!

Step 2

Cleansers can leave your skin feeling tight and dry, so use a moisturiser after cleansing to keep your skin looking healthy. This is even more important during autumn and winter - rough winds and cold weather can really damage your skin!

Top Tip

Whenever your eyes are feeling sore and tired, cut two slices of cucumber and lie back on the sofa with one slice over each eye. Lie still for 30 minutes, then remove the slices and splash your eyes with a little cold water.

Step 3

Drink plenty of water each day. There is no product in the world that is as good for your skin as pure, clear H2O!

You are supposed to drink eight glasses each day, so make sure you always have a bottle of spring water nearby.

Step 4

The sun can give your skin a beautiful, tanned glow, but it can also do a lot of damage you won't see! Always wear sunblock during the summer - and don't forget that those rays can reach your skin even on dull days!

Never leave the house without your sunnies - squinting in the sun will give you wrinkles around your eyes!

Top Tip

Go to the skincare counters in your nearest department store and ask for some advice. They are carefully trained so they'll know the best moisturiser for your skin type - and they will probably give you a few free samples to try!

Step 5

Use a face mask once every two weeks for a deep-down cleansing sensation!

Step 6

Exfoliate once every two weeks (not in the same week as your face mask), using a gentle exfoliating lotion. This scrub will leave you with a totally glam glow!

My Beauty Regime

Use this monthly planner to start your skincare regime the right way!

Each morning and evening

Cleanse

Splash cold water on face and pat dry

Moisturise

1st and 3rd Saturdays of the month

Use an exfoliating scrub to cleanse your face

Make sure all traces of the scrub are removed with warm water

Pat your face dry

Moisturise

2nd and 4th Saturdays of the month

Use a face mask for a deep-down clean

Clean your face thoroughly with warm water

Pat your face dry

Moisturise

Happenin' Hairstyles

It's great fun experimenting with different hairstyles, and it's a great way to get to 'know' your hair! Everyone's hair is different and can do different things - check out these three styles for curly hair, long and short hair!

Classic Curls

1. Give yourself a side parting.
2. Tie your hair into a low ponytail at the base of your neck with a hair band that is the same colour as your hair.
3. Twist your ponytail and let it wrap it around itself. Secure it with a second hair band.
4. Use hair grips to secure your style and keep any loose bits of hair in place.
5. Let a few ends stick out for a fresh, flirty take on a classic style.
6. Use hairspray to keep your style in place.
7. Combine this look with a classic little black dress and strappy heels!

Long and Luscious

1. Wash and towel dry your hair.
2. Work a little volumising mousse into your locks.
3. Use a hairdryer to dry your hair upside down. This will help to give it volume.
4. With your head still upside down, use a paddle brush to smooth out your hair. Then gather it into a high ponytail and secure with a hair band that is the same colour as your hair.
5. Turn your head the right way up again and check it in the mirror to make sure it looks sleek and smooth.
6. Wrap your ponytail loosely in a circle on the crown of your head. Hold it in place with hair grips and hairspray.
7. Decorate with tiny hair clips in sweet, pastel colours.

Short 'n' Stylin'

1. Wash and towel dry your hair.
2. Work some texturising gel into the roots of your hair.
3. Use a hairdryer to roughly dry your locks.
4. Rub a tiny amount of styling gel onto your hands. You will need very little — it should feel like the a thin, invisible layer all over your palms.
5. Slick back the hair at the sides of your head. Then spike up the hair on the crown of your head to give height.
6. Secure the style with firm hairspray.
7. Finish your look with dramatic, dangly earrings!

Sophisticated Shoot

Have you ever dreamed of being a model? Your dreams might just come true, so make sure you remember all the best makeup tips! Here are some of our faves!

If you want to even out your skin tone, try a tinted moisturiser for light coverage that will make your skin look luminous!

Make your eyes your stand-out feature with some clever makeup! Use eyeshadow to accentuate your natural colouring – go for a minimalist look, so no one even knows you're wearing makeup!

Use a liquid rose-coloured stain to gently bring out your natural blush – you can also use rose stain on your lips for a great natural look.

©MGA

Slick on some clear lip gloss for a bit of glamorous shine!

Always give one final glance in the mirror before heading out of the door. Check that your hair looks sleek and your makeup looks perfect, then put on a dazzlin' smile and get ready to bask in the compliments!

©MGA

To grab attention, style your hair in a totally new way. Even putting your parting in a different place can have a huge effect!

Fill a notebook with all your stylin' secrets – one day the hottest magazines may be asking for your beauty tips!

©MGA

Curl your lashes every day! Curled lashes will always give you that extra cute kick!

Check out your makeup in different lights – and make sure the mirror you use each morning gets plenty of natural light.

Stand in front of a full-length mirror and practise posing for the camera. It's not as easy as the top models make it seem! You need to look relaxed, natural and totally stylin' – and that takes practice!

©MGA

Think about your posture. The best models walk tall and proud, keeping their backs straight and their chins up.

Models always seem to have tons of confidence – but they've all got things they worry about, just like us! To look really confident, keep your muscles relaxed, smile and look people straight in the eye. If you don't feel confident inside, just pretend that you're a confident person – soon you'll find out that's exactly what you are!

©MGA

Totally Hip High

Whether you have to wear a uniform at school or you get to wear your own gear, accessories can help to make your outfit totally unique and so fashion-forward that everyone will want your new look! Use these tips to work out a look that will help you rule the school!

Use a spare notebook and get inspiration from your fashion passion to cover it — you could use cut-outs from fashion magazines or a length of some gorgeous material! This is gonna be your fashion bible, where you will write all your hottest fashion ideas, stick pics of designs that inspire you and make a note of great combos you've discovered! But first you need to make a record of the basics!

Colours
Which colours look great on you?

- Put on a white tee and sit in front of a big mirror with plenty of natural light on your face.

- Drape different coloured materials around your shoulders, one by one.

- You will see that some colours make your skin look more glowing, while some make you look pale. On one page of your fashion guidebook, write down the colours that suit you best. These will be the colours you'll wear nearest to your face - in tops, tees and scarves.

- On another page, write down the colours that don't suit you so well. These are colours you could use for skirts, shoes or trousers - nothing too close to your face! xoxo

Make a list of all the coolest accessories you have (don't forget to make a note of what colour they are!)

- Scarves
- Rings
- Necklaces
- Earrings
- Belts
- Bracelets
- Hair decorations
- Hair grips
- Hair bands
- Hair clips

Separates

If you can wear your own clothes to school, sort through your wardrobe and make a list of all the hottest separates and colours.

- List tops, tees, skirts and trousers on different pages.

- Now you can use these lists to team up items of clothing you've never put together before!

- Think daring and bold - the most unexpected combinations just might look spectacular!

- Sketch some of the possible combos in your book. xoxo

School Fashions!

©MGA

Model Magic

Colour in these models using your school colours. Now try out some accessories on them! This will help you to work out the colours and combos that go together.

Top Tip!

Use a Polaroid to take some snaps of yourself in your school gear. Then study the outfits as if you were looking at them in a fashion mag. What could you add to make them unique and super-stylin'?

Hot Hair

Experiment with your hairstyle and make a note of how you made certain styles work. List the styling products you used and the hair accessories you teamed them with.

Standout from the Crowd

Do you have an awesome collection of necklaces or bracelets? Do your friends always ask to borrow your scarves or hair grips? What's your fashion passion?

Manicure your nails once a week and use them like mini canvases. Paint them differently each week and soon everyone will be eager to see your latest designs!

XOXO

If your school doesn't have a uniform, you've got even more choice! Use the models to design some sizzlin' combinations using the separates and accessories you've got in your wardrobe!

Best Friends 4ever

Hi, i'm Cloe and i'm gonna tell you about something totally amazing that happened to me and my best friends - just because we're best friends!

We were sipping smoothies at our fave pavement café after a game of tennis. Jade had been with us, but then she'd got a call on her mobile and had dashed off immediately. (Luckily Fianna had been at the tennis courts so we teamed up with her instead.) Jade had arranged to meet us at the café - but there was still no sign of her!

"What do you think that call was about?" asked Sasha for the millionth time.
"I don't know, Bunny Boo!" I repeated with a smile.
"You can't know everything, you know!"
"I can try!" Sasha said with a laugh.
"It's totally mysterious though," Yasmin continued. "Whatever it was, she was really excited - and it takes something super cool to get Jade moving like that!"
See, Kool Kat is famous for her laid-back attitude. Just then we saw Jade sauntering down the pavement towards us.
"What's the buzz?" I asked her as she slid into a seat. I pushed a banana smoothie towards her and she sipped it gratefully.
™ "Thanks - I totally needed that!"

"So come on, spill!" Sasha demanded.

Jade's green eyes twinkled. "I have got the most spectacular surprise ever for you guys!"

"Kool Kat!" we all yelled.

"OK, OK!" she replied. "You know that exclusive fashion show we read about last week?"

"The one that it was, like, totally impossible to get tickets for?" I sighed.

"There's no such word as 'impossible'," Jade said, raising her eyebrows at me. I gave a loud squeal that made Sasha wince!

"No way! Jade, are you serious? You got tickets for that red-hot show?"

"I got five!" Jade told us. "So you can come too, Fianna - if you want to."

"Just try to stop me!" said Fianna excitedly.

"They're front-row seats too," Jade added. "I know a girl who's doing an internship at the fashion house... and luckily she owes me a favour."

"This is gonna be awesome!" exclaimed Yasmin, fanning herself with a café menu. "We're gonna be centre stage at the hottest fashion show of the season!"

"Well, now we know what we're doing this afternoon!" said Sasha.

"Shopping!" we yelled together. We all needed some sophisticated new outfits to make sure we looked super-stylin' at the show!

©MGA

©MGA

We counted the hours until the day of the show. Early that morning we met up at Jade's house to perfect our looks, then gathered in front of the full-length mirror, arm in arm.

"Do you think we look trendsettin' enough?" asked Yasmin.

"Girl," I said, "heads are gonna turn!"

We arrived at the show and handed our embossed invitations to the doormen. Even they looked runway ready! Inside, the atmosphere was buzzing with anticipation and there was glitz 'n' glamour everywhere we looked! We recognised a group of super-stylin' designers and spotted the fashion editor of our fave magazine.

"This is like a dream come true!" I squealed, nudging Yasmin in the side. Fianna gasped as a supermodel glided past us.

"Total star quality," I heard Jade muttering under her breath.

"Come on, you guys, let's grab our seats!" said Sasha in her best 'let's get organised' tone of voice. Jade rolled her eyes at me - we love Bunny Boo but she can be a bit of control freak sometimes! We followed her as she led the way to our front-row seats.

ODMTT 1

©MGA

64

There was a stylin' programme-
of-events booklet on our
seats, and we each picked
one up eagerly and
started to read.
    "You guys, check
this out!" said
Yasmin, pointing
to the intro page of
the booklet. "The theme of
the show is 'Lilli & Titch - Best
Friends Forever'!"
We all grinned at each other. The two
designers behind the show, Lilliane and
Titchka, were best friends. They had
set up a fashion label and designed a
range of A-list styles that would look
dazzlin' together - without being too
matchy-matchy.

    "Check this out!" said Jade, reading
further down the page. "They've chosen models
who are best friends too! They're convinced it'll
create a fantastic vibe on stage!"
    "Totally," agreed Sasha. "I'll bet the models will
show off the fashions even better when they're
surrounded by their friends!"
    "Can you imagine how super cool it must be
to have a job that you can do with all your
best friends?" said Fianna.
    "That would be a real dream job!" agreed
Yasmin with a big smile.
    Just then the lights dimmed,
there was a burst of
music and people
rushed to their seats...
the show was about
to start!

PROGRAMME

BEST FRIENDS
4ever

©MGA

65

The show began with a burst of golden sparkles as all five models stepped out onto the catwalk, arm in arm and side by side. The fashions were full of diva attitude - totally sophisticated! I could just imagine striking a pose in one low-slung skirt, which swirled around the model's legs in a stunning silky textured fabric.

I had my sketchpad on my knees and was dashing off sketches of the designs as fast as my pencil would go! Jade kept leaning across Fianna's legs towards me and whispering, "Make sure you sketch that one, Angel! Ooh, don't miss this cute lil' bustier top! Did you sketch those pearly heels yet?"

"I'd sketch a whole lot faster if you'd let me concentrate!" I exclaimed, shooting her a grin to let her know I was teasing.

It was so exciting! I knew I was gonna remember this day for the rest of my life! We were all inspired by the catwalk glamour, and I was getting tons of new fashion ideas.

The only black spot was when one of the models twisted her ankle as she gave a spin. Her friends rushed over to her and helped her limp off the catwalk.

66

©MGA

After a glittering finale, where gold and silver stars rained down on the audience, the show came to an end and there was a storm of applause. We stayed in our seats for a while as people started to leave - I wanted to finish a couple of sketches and Jade was scribbling ideas in her little 'inspirations' notebook. Sasha stood up and started to fidget. "Come on, you guys," she said eventually. "Let's get to the mall and start shopping - I'm bursting with new ideas!"

"Chill, Bunny Boo," said Jade. "We won't be long."

Sasha strolled off to the side of the catwalk. I finished my sketches and looked up at the others.

"OK, ready to go!"

Just then, Sasha came dashing over to us, her eyes bright with excitement.

"You guys have gotta see this! Check it out!"

We followed her over to the corner of the room. The door to the backstage area was wide open!

"Let's peek inside!" said Sasha, bold as ever. "How often are we gonna get the chance to find out what goes on behind the scenes at a fashion show?"

Yasmin and Fianna hung back, but Jade, Sasha and I peered through the doorway. What we saw made us gasp in amazement!

©MGA

It was pandemonium! The famous designers were surrounded by worried-looking photographers, journalists and stylists. "What are we going to do?" exclaimed, Lilli, one of the designers. "This is a disaster!"

"What's happened?" asked Sasha in a loud voice. I thought they were going to yell at us for crashing backstage, but they just turned to look at us.

"Our models were supposed to go straight from the show into a fashion shoot," explained the other designer, Titchka.

"It's for a major magazine, added Lilli. "But the model who hurt her ankle has gone to hospital - and all her best friends have gone with her!"

"Which we totally understand," added Titchka. "They are her best friends - but they're also our models and it means that we're in a jam!"

Just then, Yasmin and Fianna poked their heads into the room too. We filled them in on what had happened.

"We should go," said Yasmin. "They don't want people hanging around while they're in such a mess!"

But Titchka was staring at us with her mouth open!

"There are five of you?" she exclaimed.

"We're best friends," I explained. "We came to see the show."

©MGA

68

Titchka swooped down on is and swept us into the room, suddenly buzzing with energy. I could almost see sparks coming off her! The stylists and photographers were looking as bewildered as we felt, but Lilli seemed to be able to read her best friend's mind!

"Perfect!" she cried. "They already look super stylin' - they just might be able to save the shoot!"

"One of my more brilliant ideas!" Titchka exclaimed (she kinda reminded me of Sasha!)

"Excuse me!" said Sasha loudly. "What's going on?"

Titchka turned to us, her eyes sparkling with excitement.

"See, we had five models and the photo shoot is all about our 'Best Friends Forever' line - so we really need five best friends to model the clothes..."

We all gasped. "You mean... us?" I asked, hardly able to believe my ears.

"Will you do it - please?" asked Lilli.

Can you believe it? She was actually begging us to be on the cover of a fashion mag!

"Yes!" we all said at the same time.

Within seconds we were whisked into a dressing room where the stylists asked us to sit down in front of the long mirror.

©MGA

The stylists got to work on our locks, giving us styles that looked super individual but fitted together perfectly too. "Your hair is super silky," the stylist told me, "so it's gonna look fabulous just hanging loose down your back. But I'll give the ends a little curl for that angelic vibe!"

Fianna's hair was straightened and then turned under at the ends for a style that looked truly sleek and chic. Jade's black mane was given lift and body with extra large curlers.

Sasha was given a simple, sophisticated style that made her hair seem even more glossy than usual, while Yasmin's stylist put lil' flicks into her locks and moved her parting to give her a totally new look. We picked up some awesome secret tips from the professionals!

Next it was time for our makeup to be done for us. We've done so many makeovers on each other that we are super chilled about letting someone loose with the eyeliner - and these guys really knew what they were doing!

The makeup artist started with an ivory foundation shade for me, which made my skin look utterly flawless. Then he coloured my eyelids with the palest of pale blue powder, which really highlighted the colour of my eyes.

My eyes were outlined with a super-thin line of black liquid eyeliner, then my eyelashes were curled and brushed with black mascara. My eyes looked tons larger! Next he chose a deep pink shade for my lips and matched it with a blush for the apples of my cheeks. He worked so fast it was amazing - and his work was awesome! I've never had such a fabulous makeover!

Everyone's makeup looked stunning and natural - and we all wanted to try it for ourselves! At last it was time to try on the fashions! I was given the low-slung skirt I had loved on the catwalk, and it was teamed with a hip lil' cami top in the same fabric. I think Jade wanted to wear everything! But soon we were all wearing glam, sophisticated outfits that made us feel like real models!

"OK, girls, strike a pose!" called the head photographer as he set up his lights and positioned us in front of a screen. "Think passion! Think panache! Think star quality!" "Think best friends!" cried Lilli and Titch, who were being interviewed on the other side of the room.

©MGA

©MGA

We had the most amazing afternoon ever! We struck elegant poses in our outfits and it felt fabulous to be in the limelight like that! The photographer went through several rolls of film, snapping countless pics as we pouted and strutted. Every few minutes the hair and makeup artists would rush up to us and adjust any stray locks or correct any makeup that was slipping.

"We need these guys with us all the time!" joked Jade as her hair was combed back into place.

©MGA

But this dream afternoon couldn't last forever, and finally the shoot was over and the photographers were packing up. Lilli and Titch rushed over to us.

"We can't thank you guys enough!" said Lilli.

"Yeah, you completely saved the day!" Titch agreed. "So we'd like to give you something to show our appreciation!"

"You don't have to do that!" I cried. "This has been an awesome day for us - and we've learned tons of tips from the stylists!"

"That's great," said Lilli with a smile. "But we would also like you to keep the outfits you wore for the shoot - it's the least we can do!"

©MGA

I squealed in excitement and Sasha gave a whoop! Even Jade raised her eyebrows and gave a little smile!
"Thank you so much!" I cried, hugging our new friends.

On the day the magazine came out, we were first into the shop to buy it! We each got a copy and we stared at it in amazement - we were actually on the cover! I had to pinch myself to make sure that I wasn't dreaming!
"We're cover girls!" cried Fianna in delight. "Check it out - we look like total divas!"

There was a full article inside too, all about Lilli and Titch's fashion label. But right at the end of the article, it mentioned our names and said that we had saved the day!
"Well," said Jade, closing the magazine and grinning at us all. "I thought that nothing could be more sensational than getting tickets to that show..."
"But the show turned out even more fabulous than we could have imagined!" Cloe finished.
"That's why it's so fantastic to have such awesome best friends!" I exclaimed.
"Best friends forever!" we chorused.

BRATZ

Passion 4 Fashion

Flaunt it, or forget it!

Design tips from Yasmin

Sasha at work!

FAB FRESH new!

Fashionistas Unite!

© MGA

Find Your Dream Career!

Sasha's Guide to Finding Your Dream Career
We are always talking about our future careers — some of us know exactly what we want to do and some of us change our plans each week (you know who you are, Cloe!) If you're not sure what you want to do, take this quiz and see which career you'd suit!

1. You hit the mall with your best friends - which shop do you make a beeline for first?

a. The bookshop - to check out the latest releases.

b. The electronics shop - I love my girly gadgets!

c. The budget clothes shop - their stock changes each week and they are full of up-to-the minute copies of the latest styles on the catwalk.

d. The most expensive clothes shop in the mall - they always have the most unique fashions!

e. The music shop - I always listen to the latest singles to keep up with the hottest new tracks.

f. The makeup counters of the department store - to see what special offers are on and keep my beauty collection growing! XOXO

2 good + 2 be 4 gotten ... cause i c ... ends 4 ever- ... ROCKS!

2. You're looking forward to your holiday this year — but where are you going?

a. I'm not having a holiday this year - instead I'm grabbing the chance to get some work experience at my fave magazine.

b. Somewhere stunningly beautiful - I want to take some totally awesome snaps!

c. One of the great capital cities of the world - to check out where the latest fashion trends are born!

d. I'm hitting a little-known spot where all the stars congregate - you have to be in with the in-crowd to know about it!

e. I'm building my holiday around the hottest concert of the year - I've got the best tickets of course!

f. I'm spending my holiday with my friends - I love just being around them and sharing secrets. XOXO

3. You're at a fashion show with your friends — what's grabbing your attention?

a. The famous faces in the front row - who's with who and what they're doing - I love being first to find out the celebrity gossip.

b. Whatever I see through the viewfinder of my camera!

c. The new trends that are being started on the catwalk - I'm sketching everything in my notepad to inspire me when I get home.

d. The way the models walk and show off the clothes - they look super-elegant!

e. The music the designers have chosen - I like trying to figure out why they chose those tracks!

f. The extreme makeup that the models are wearing - it's just as inspiring as the fashion designs!

4. What's your fave class at school and why?

a. I love History because I like finding out the truth behind historical and political events.

b. Media studies - it's super exciting to use all the different cameras and recorders and make my own images!

c. I always look forward to art 'cuz I like being able to make a picture with just a few strokes of my pencil.

d. It's gotta be my language classes - being able to speak other languages makes travelling way easier!

e. I love music - I would like to be able to play every sort of instrument!

f. I enjoy P.E. because I like to keep fit and healthy.

5. You have a day to pamper yourself - what do you choose to do?

a. Relax in a sauna with the latest magazines.

b. Spend the morning taking artistic black-and-white snaps, then the afternoon developing them in my own dark room.

c. Shop shop shop! \

d. Kick back with my best girls, swapping beauty tips and reading the celebrity gossip pages.

e. Wander around a huge music shop in the morning, picking out some awesome CDs, then spend the afternoon transferring them to my MP3 player.

f. Go to the beauty salon with my best friends for manis, pedis and gossip!

6. It's a rainy day and your friends aren't around, so you've curled up in a cosy armchair with something to read — what is it?

a. Today's newspaper - I like to be on top of what's going on.

b. A collection of award-winning images by my fave photographers.

c. A pile of fashion mags - and my notebook to write down ideas if I get inspired. \

d. A fat modern novel about the rich and famous - it'll be me one day!

e. My fave monthly music journal - it tells me what albums are due out soon, so I'm always one step ahead.

f. Hair magazines - I love checking out the up-to-the-minute hairstyles. XOXO

7. Which of these sentences describes you best?

a. I like to keep my finger on the pulse and I'm always the first to know the latest hot gossip.

b. I have boxes and albums full of photos - it's my fave way to keep my memories fresh!

c. I love to customise my own clothes and people always ask me where I bought them!

d. I'm a total drama queen and I love getting attention! \

e. I can always predict which song is gonna be number one - and which new bands are gonna be stars.

f. My friends always come to me with their problems - they think I'm great at giving advice!

Scores:

Mostly As: Journalist,
Mostly Bs: Photographer,
Mostly Cs: Fashion designer,
Mostly Ds: Actress,
Mostly Es: Music producer,
Mostly Fs: Makeup artist

©MGA

Sparkle 'n' Shine

Making jewellery is a great way to relax and be creative at the same time! When you understand the basics, you can make pretty much anything! You will be able to make the perfect necklace to wear with you latest fashion find, and you'll never be stuck for presents!

You will need:

A set of pliers - cutters for snipping wire and round-nosed pliers for shaping wire into loops. (Ask an adult to help you out by showing you how to use the cutters!)
Beads
Thin silver wire
Earring wires
Screw clasps
Special beading thread
Hair slide
Visit your nearest bead shop for some inspiration!

Basic Skills

- Grab your round-nosed pliers and a small piece of wire. Now practise making loops! They won't be perfect at first, but if you keep trying you will soon be making perfect circles with the wire!

- Practise tying tiny, strong knots.

- Play around with beads of various sizes. Check out the colours, sizes and styles of bead that work well together.

©MGA

Pendant Necklace

The easiest type of necklace to make is a pendant necklace.

1. Choose a single, beautiful bead that will hang on its own around your neck. Pick a pendant bead that already has a hole in it.

2. Make a small loop with a piece of wire, then cut the wire end off with the cutters. You will be left with a small circle of wire.

3. Open the circle wide enough to join it on to the pendant, then close it again.

4. Feed the thread you have chosen through the loop.

5. Tie the thread to a screw clasp to finish off your necklace!

Earrings

1. Pick out two beads that match your pendant necklace, but are smaller.

2. Make two small loops with a piece of wire, then cut the wire ends off with the cutters. You will be left with two small circles of wire.

3. Open the circles with the round-nosed pliers and join each one onto a bead. Then close the circles again.

4. Use your round-nosed pliers to slightly open the loop on the earring wires.

5. Carefully put the beads onto the earring wires, then close up the loops with your pliers.

6. If you are making earrings for pierced ears, sterilise the earring wire before you put it into your ear.

Hair Slide

1. Tie a knot in the end of your thread, leaving a long tail of thread.

2. Add one large bead and then feed the thread through the hole at one end of the hair slide.

3. Add another large bead so that there is a bead on each side of the hole.

4. This is the fun part! Feed enough beads onto your thread to fill the length of the hair slide. Think about the colour combinations you want to use and the styles you're gonna team the slide with. You could mix some really unusual colours and choose some plain and some sparkly beads!

5. When you reach the hole at the other end of the hair slide, add a third large bead. Then pass the thread through the hole and add a fourth large bead.

6. Feed the thread back up through the hole and through the third large bead.

7. Now you can add another length of decorative beads to make your hair slide brighter and more dazzlin'!

8. When you reach the other end of the slide, feed your thread through the hole and then back up through one of the large beads.

9. You can add as many rows of beads as you like by repeating steps 7 and 8.

10. When you have enough beads, pass the thread down through the first hole and tie a knot with the long tail of thread you left at the start.

Fashion Adventure

Hi, i'm Sasha, and my story is gonna rock your world! it all started because we were in Byron Powell's new reality TV show, America Rocks Fashion. Byron was worried. The head of the network was going to cancel his show unless it had more drama and thrills!

Byron stepped in front of a camera. "Welcome to America Rocks Fashion! Byron Powell here in beautiful Stilesville to launch the season finale's adventure in fashion! Somewhere out there in the heartland of America, a teen fashion designer waits to be discovered. It's Wednesday morning and our two teams, rival fashion magazines Your Thing and Bratz, set out today with their travelling runways to find her. They'll visit three small towns, each team picking one girl per town. The teams have to get their chosen girls to New York by Saturday night. There, the six contestants will model their own fashions in the America Rocks Fashion show. The winner gets a contract with fashion designer Mucci Fiari and her own pair of diamond go-go boots! Absolutely, positively priceless!"

©MGA

"Here's our first team - Bratz Magazine!" A catwalk folded out of our truck and I came strutting out with my best girls, smiling and waving, while the live audience applauded wildly.

"...and the competing team - Your Thing Magazine, represented by Burdine Maxwell," said Byron. The back of a huge pink truck opened up and Burdine walked out on another catwalk.

"Don't forget us!" squeaked Kaycee and we groaned - the Tweevils were there too!

During the commercial break, Cloe complained that she hated road trips. "Don't you know what happens on the open road?" she cried.

"What happens on the open road, Cloe?" asked Byron curiously.

"You know," said Cloe. "Alien encounters, that guy with the hook who tries to get in your car... that cute stray dog that turns out to really be a rat... the headless horseman."

"Get ahold of yourself, Drama Mama!" I exclaimed, giving Angel a shake.

But Byron seemed interested. "Alien encounters, you say? Seems absolutely, positively exciting to me!"

Byron took his place in front of the camera.
"A rustic road trip - no cell phones allowed, no GPS, just a map. Thrilling. Start your engines, ladies!"

©MGA

We started off
feeling totally
pumped to be on
the road together!
But later that day we weren't
so wired! The open road
turned out to be super boring!
"The things we do for Byron," Cloe said.
I reminded her of all the cool experiences
we'd had since we met him. "Byron's my total
role model," I said. "Think of all he's
accomplished!"

Just then, Cloe saw a hitchhiker. He
looked totally creepy, with a bandana
pulled up to his eyes and a tattered
hat. The rest of us didn't see him,
but later, as we were driving down
a lonely highway, Cloe saw the very
same creepy hitchhiker standing at
the side of the road!

"Did you see that?" Cloe squealed. "I just saw
the same hitchhiker I saw an hour ago!"
We all looked up, but there was no one in the road.
We thought Cloe was imagining things!
"I'm not crazy!" Cloe yelled.
"Lets pull over at the next stop," Yasmin suggested.

At the next stop, Cloe headed
for the toilets on her own - and
saw the hitchhiker again! She led
us around the side of the
building, but no one was
there. We all thought
Cloe was flipping out!

80

©MGA

That night and the next day, Cloe kept seeing the hitchhiker - and we were getting really worried about her. Finally we reached Willoughby Springs, the first town on our route. Byron was waiting for us there, and we had to choose our first contestant for the competition.

We chose a girl called Mandy Pickett. Mandy, a cute girl in a cowboy hat and fringed top, came to join us.

Burdine announced that she had chosen a girl called Christy Baker. Christy was super stuck up and had a totally fake French accent - but worst of all, she looked exactly like the Tweevils!
"Now they're Treevils," said Yasmin in horror.

Soon we were back on the open road, this time with Mandy in the front seat.
"I'm so excited ya'll picked me," said Mandy. "It's a dream come true. Thank you!"
We kept driving until we spotted a café and stopped for something to eat. Unfortunately, Burdine had the same idea! We all headed into the café.

The café's waitress was called Dot. She was a huge woman with thick, hairy legs. Mandy went to the toilet while we ordered some food. We didn't know that outside, someone was sabotaging one of the trucks!

©MGA

81

Dot warned us not to pick up any hitchhikers and told us about a ghost called Foul-mouthed Foley, who would haunt you forever if you saw him. We all sat and stared at each other as Dot went back to the kitchen.

"No way, just a tall tale," I said. We went to look for Mandy and found her outside, but when we turned back to the café, something was weird. The café was now in darkness.

"They couldn't have closed," said Yasmin. "We didn't pay."

Jade put her hand on the door and slowly opened it. The whole diner was covered with spiders' webs and dust - it looked as if it had been empty for years!

"Let's get out of here!" yelled Cloe.

"We're so sorry we didn't believe you, Cloe," I said as soon as we were safely away from the café.

"Guys, this is just like every story I've heard about creepy trips on the open road," said Cloe. "I want to go home."

"But we're supposed to be in Mount Middleton in an hour," said Yasmin. Mandy started to cry - she thought we were giving up. We promised that we would get her to the competition - and that she would be fabulous!

182

©MGA

Burdine's truck was heading for Mount Middleton when there was a loud bang and the truck swerved. They had a flat tyre - someone had put nails in it! Christy had had enough, so she called her father and he came to take her home. Burdine had lost her only contestant!

In Mount Middleton ours was the only team that turned up. We chose our contestant - a girl called Tiffany. But before we could take her with us, we found out that she had been stealing from us! So we left Mount Middleton with just one contestant.

Burdine thought that we had put the nails in her tyre - like we'd stoop so low! She swapped some roads signs around so that we'd go the wrong way, and soon we were driving past farmland.

"I hate cornfields," said Cloe. "Aliens are really drawn to them."

We were totally lost - we had to spend the night in the truck!

In the morning we found that we were in the middle of a cornfield.

"Oh no!" Cloe wailed. "Look where we are! There could be aliens all around us, closing in."

Just then we heard a weird noise in the corn. I took a deep breath and moved forward to investigate.

©MGA

As we crept forward, the sound got louder. Then we heard noises from behind us as well!

"They're surrounding us!" Cloe whispered.

"Run!" I yelled.

We burst out into a clearing and saw a huge figure right in front of us - it looked just like an alien! We screamed and fell to the ground!

"What's going on?" said Mandy's voice behind us.

We opened our eyes, squinting in the sun. The creepy figure was a scarecrow, dressed in a super-cool T-shirt and jeans. A girl was peeking out from behind the scarecrow - we had scared her just as much as she scared us!

We introduced ourselves to the girl, who was called Sharidan. She recognised us because she was a big fan of America Rocks Fashion!

That's when Jade noticed the outfit on the scarecrow. It was the best-dressed scarecrow we had ever seen - and it turned out that Sharidan had made the outfit!

"Fabulous," I said. "That's super stylin'." We all looked at each other. "Are we having a cosmic thought convergence?" I asked.

"I'm thinking we just found our second contestant!" said Jade.

We stayed the night at Sharidan's house and persuaded her parents to let her come with us to New York.

In the morning, Mandy was acting totally weird about Sharidan. "She's not really model material," Mandy said.

"Well, each person has their own style," said Cloe. "That's what fashion is all about, taking risks and expressing yourself," Jade chimed in. "No matter what anyone else thinks."

But while we were saying goodbye to Sharidan's parents, Mandy took the truck - with all of Sharidan's fashions on board! We realised that it must have been Mandy all along - she framed the girl in Mount Middleton, and she probably put the nails in Burdine's tyre! Luckily, Mrs Jones had a car that we could borrow. We piled in and headed for New York - we had to get Sharidan's fashions back from Mandy, and tell Byron that she was a car thief and saboteur!

As we were powering along the highway, we saw the hitchhiker up ahead! "It's Foul-mouthed Foley!" I screamed. But Cloe decided that she had to face her fear. She got out of the car and ran towards Foul-mouthed-Foley. He started to run away, but Cloe was too fast for him. She ripped his bandana off - it was Byron!

©MGA

©MGA

81

A camera crew came out from behind a hedge.
"What is going on, Byron?" I demanded.
"It's going to air in the season finale tonight," Byron explained. "I needed something to make the show more exciting. So... I've been filming yours and Burdine's exciting encounters on the road with ghosts, aliens, hitchhikers... America's urban legends and the like."
"You used us!" gasped Yasmin.
"So the ghost town..." Jade began.
"Yes," said Byron. "I was Dot."

We were so angry that we forgot to mention Mandy. Just then, one of the assistants stepped forward. "Mr Powell, we've got to leave for New York City."
The sound of a helicopter drowned out our voices. Before we could do anything to stop him, Byron and his crew had hopped into the helicopter and were gone!

At the show, Byron told Burdine that he had been the alien leader she had met the night before. Burdine thought he meant that he really was an alien! She ran onto the catwalk.
"It's him!" she screamed. "He's the alien leader! Everybody run!"
The audience just laughed and Burdine was taken away by two attendants in white coats!

That's when we arrived at the show - just in time to see Mandy sauntering down the catwalk in Sharidan's fashions!

©MGA

We rushed over to Byron and told him what had happened. He said that we could enter Sharidan in the competition - but that meant she had to have her fashions ready in just 20 minutes!

"I can't design clothes in 20 minutes!" she cried.

"What's wrong with what you're wearing?" I asked.

"Yeah," said Cloe. "That's the outfit we fell in love with when we met you."

"It's so much more unique and original than what Mandy stole," said Jade.

After 20 minutes of hard work, Sharidan had the outfits ready! She stepped out onto the catwalk. As the audience gasped and applauded her outfit, she gained confidence and really started groovin' to the music! Then we came out, all wearing Sharidan's designs! The audience went crazy!

When the votes started to come in, at first Mandy was ahead, but at the last minute Sharidan's votes overtook Mandy's. Sharidan had won!

But before Byron could present Sharidan with the diamond go-go boots, Mandy snatched them, pulled them on and ran away!

Byron apologised for tricking us and promised not to use the footage he had filmed.

"I was wrong," he said. "Can you forgive me?"

"Sure, Byron," I replied. "But we've got some boots to get back!"

©MGA

We chased Mandy all through the streets of Manhattan and into the subway! We raced down into the subway as a train pulled into the station. Mandy jumped on board and so did we - but just before the doors closed, she jumped off again! We were stuck on the train as it pulled out!

On the platform, Mandy turned to find Sharidan standing next to her. Mandy jumped down onto the tracks! Sharidan followed her down and gave chase. As they drew near to the next station, Sharidan saw us on the platform.
"Run, Sharidan!" Cloe yelled. A train was coming up behind her!
Suddenly one Diamond Go-Go boot got stuck in the track! Sharidan pulled Mandy out of the way in the nick of time - just as the train whisked by!

Byron's camera operator had caught the whole thing on film, and Byron showed it as part of the final show. Mandy was taken away by the police!

©MGA

We were hanging in the TV lounge watching the show when Byron walked in. "Mucci Fiari has just asked me a favour," he told us. "He wanted to know if I'd use my persuasion to get you ladies to agree to model his new winter line for a photo spread. What do you say?" What do you think we said, sistah? "WOOOO HOOOO!"

The photo shoot was done on the ice rink at Rockefeller Center. The photographer snapped away at our stylin' poses. Then Byron came over to chat to us. "Thanks to your exciting pursuit of Miss Mandy, our season finale was the most successful reality show on air! The network wants to do a whole new season!" "That's fantastic!" said Cloe.

Just then a car pulled up and we saw Sharidan's parents - it was time to say goodbye to our new friend! We waved and blew kisses as they drove away. Then we turned to Byron, who was holding a limo door open for us.
"Ladies, it's our last afternoon and there's only one thing we haven't covered in New York City," he said.
We looked at each other and exclaimed, "Shopping!"

©MGA

I ♡ BOYZ

Awesome

have a super
take care ca...
...rien
...hion

Do you always mean to keep a diary— and never get around to it? Life's too busy to write in your diary every night, but here are some super-cool ways to preserve your coolest high-school memories!

Glue ™

You'll need:

- A blank A4-sized hard-covered notebook
- A plain photo frame
- A plain photo album
- Glue
- A collection of your fave accessories, e.g. glitter, bows, ribbons, silk, faux fur, cuttings from your fave mags
- Card
- All your photos from the past year

- Gold-foil wrapping paper
- Notes from your friends
- Old concert tickets from your top gigs
- Your fave perfume
- Envelopes
- A few sheets of writing paper
- Cards, letters, song words, keyrings and anything else that reminds you of great times you had over the past year!

Memory Book

First you're gonna create a memory book! In this yearbook you can record all the fun things you've done over the past year, so you'll never forget them!

- Allow two pages of the book for each memory. Stick the pictures, notes and tickets onto the pages.
- Spray the perfume you were wearing that day onto a piece of card. Put the perfume card and anything else that can't be stuck onto the page into an envelope. Then stick the envelope onto the page too.
- Write a few lines about the memory in a corner of the page. Soon your book will be bulging with memories!
- Use some of the material, ribbons and glitter to cover the outside of your memory book and make it totally unique.
- Design a gorgeous title page with your name and the date on it.
- Think about all the memories you'd like to record and make a list of them. Separate all the items you have gathered into memory piles. Put together everything that will remind you of a day or event - hair decorations you wore, snaps you took, notes you wrote to your friends or the words of a song you danced to. Or maybe you picked a flower and pressed it, or found an unusual leaf.
- Finally, when your book of memories is full, find a quiet spot and write a letter - to yourself! You're gonna seal up this letter and open it again in one year's time. Write anything you want. Tell yourself things you think you might have forgotten in a year's time. Write down your deepest secrets and remind yourself of everything you've been doing lately
- Put your letter into an envelope and seal it. Write on the front the date you are allowed to open it up. Now stick the envelope on the last page of your memory book - and put it away for a year. When you open it again, the memories will come flooding back to you!

©MGA

yeah
i care...
r for ev
ks!

Accessories!

JASMIN™

XOXO

©MGA

Photo Frame

- Cover the edges of the photo frame in your fave material. Try faux-fur animal prints for a retro-cool look!

- Choose some photos of your best friends. You will need a good, clear picture of each friend's face. Each picture will have to be small enough to fit inside the star shape. Pick a picture of yourself, too.

- Glue each picture onto a piece of card.

- Trace the star shape over each photo, so that each face is in the middle of a star.

- Carefully cut out the star shapes and use glue to stick them around the edge of the photo frame.

- Now choose a photo of you and all your friends together, and put it into the frame. Keep the frame on your dressing table or desk so your friends are always with you! These make great presents, too!

©MGA

Photo Album

My Photo Album

- Use the gold-foil wrapping paper to cover your album. It will look totally dazzlin'!

- Use a stencil to write the words 'My Photo Album' on a piece of card in pencil. Then colour in the words. You could decorate them with pictures of flowers, fashions or your fave animal! Stick the card onto the front of the album.

- Think about what's most important to you. Whatever it is, use that as a theme to decorate your album. If you're lovin' a certain band at the moment, decorate your album with pics from magazines, CD covers and concert tickets. If your friends are the most important part of your life, cover your album with hand-drawn portraits of your best girls! You could do the same with movie stars, pets, book or fashion! Just make sure the cover reflects what you're all about!

- Now you can fill the album with the rest of your photos! Use a gold pen to write the date and occasion of each photo.

Glam Games

Sleepovers are always great fun, but if you prepare a few games for your best girls, you'll just be giggling all evening! Check out our fave sleepover games for the most hilarious slumber party ever!

Musical Nail Varnish!

1. Choose one person to control the music.
2. Sit in a circle and pass a bottle of nail varnish around until the music stops.
3. When the music stops, the girl who has the bottle must paint as many toenails as she can before the music starts again.
4. As soon as the music starts, pass the bottle around again.
5. The first person with all ten toes painted is the winner!

Who Am I?

1. Sit in a circle and give each person a small square of card and a pen.
2. Ask each of your friends to write the name of a famous person on the card.
3. Without letting them see the name you've written, stick the card on the forehead of the girl next to you.
4. Now each person has to try to guess who they are! Take it in turns to ask one question – but you can only ask questions that have a 'yes' or 'no' answer!
5. Keep going until everyone has guessed who they are!

Mirrorless Makeover Challenge!

1. Give each girl some eyeshadow, eyeliner, lipstick and cream blush.
2. Each contestant has to apply her makeup as perfectly as she can – in just 30 seconds, without looking in a mirror! Set the timer on your mobile so you know when 30 seconds is up.
3. When you have finished, bring out a mirror and check out your handiwork!
4. Make sure you take some snaps of all the contestants!

©MGA

Tasty Treats

One of the best things about having a sleepover is all the yummy snacks you get to try out. Raid the kitchen and throw together some of our fave treats. With these ideas, you're sure to have a totally delicious night!

Pizza Toast

You'll need:
Thick-sliced bread • Tomato puree • Oregano • Sweetcorn • Black and green olives • Jalapeno peppers • Cheese, grated

Here's how:

1. This is a great quick savoury snack and totally yummy!

2. Toast the slices of bread.

3. Spread tomato puree onto the toast quite thickly, making sure you cover all the edges.

4. Sprinkle some oregano thinly over the puree.

5. Add a layer of sweetcorn and a few thin slices of green and black olives. Add a little jalapeno pepper if you like hot things!

Sprinkle with grated cheese and place under the grill until the cheese has melted. Then season, cut into quarters and serve!

Delicious Drinks

Serve creamy smoothies early in the evening, and mugs of frothy hot chocolate just before you turn out the lights!

Sweet Treat!

Hide some lollipops around your room and have a lollipop hunt! Make sure you hide them really well and time the hunt so that your friends have just one minute to find the sweets. Take some snaps of them as they're hunting too – you'll enjoy looking back at all the fun you had!

©MGA

Fabulous & Fruity

Create a colourful platter of delicious fruits – get super creative with your display and make it so tempting that not a single piece of fruit will be left! Combine jewel colours like ruby-red strawberries and cool-green kiwi fruit.

Perfect Pitta

Cut pitta bread into strips and fan it around a plate, with a tub of your fave dip in the middle.

Guacamole

Home-made guacamole is way tastier than the brands you can buy in the shops! It is quick and easy – and totally delicious!

You'll need:
Three ripe avocados • 1 small clove of garlic, crushed • Hot pepper sauce • Sour cream • Lemon juice • Salt and pepper

Here's how:

1. Cut each avocado in half and remove the stone.

2. Use a spoon to take the flesh out and mash roughly with a fork.

3. Add the garlic, pepper sauce, lemon juice and mash them in with the fork.

4. Add a little sour cream and stir it in with a spoon.

5. Add a few grains of salt and pepper to taste.

6. Serve with crisps and vegetable sticks!

On Ice ™

Hi, my name's Yasmin and i'm gonna tell you about a totally cool adventure i had – and how it helped me realise how much my friends mean to me!

"I wanted to practise with the cheerleading team today," sighed Sasha, staring out at the snowy scene.

"Why did it have to snow today?" said Jade with a groan. "I was gonna head down to that new boutique in the mall, but everything is shut because of the weather!"

"You guys, we've got a surprise day off!" I reminded them. "Why aren't we getting ready to do something spectacular?"

"It's too cold to do anything spectacular," Cloe complained, shifting her chair closer to the fire.

©MGA

What's with this attitude?" I asked, glancing outside. "The snow is making everything look totally magical!"

"Yeah," said Jade, popping a chocolate into her mouth and grinning at me. "As long as we stay this side of the window, Pretty Princess!"

"No way," I replied, standing up and putting my hands on my hips. "How about going ice skating? That's great fun - and we'll be able to actually enjoy the weather instead of complaining about it!"

But I was met with three totally uninspired faces.

"It's too cold," said Jade, curling up in her armchair like a cat.

"I just wanna relax here," Cloe added, snuggling in amongst the cushions.

"I am so not up for trekking through the snow," said Sasha with a wide yawn.

I looked down at them all, feeling a bit annoyed. After all, how often do you get a free day off from school?

"Well, I'm gonna go," I announced. My best friends didn't move a muscle.

"Fine," I said, trying not to sound too annoyed. "I'm sure I'll find someone to skate with at the rink. I'll see you guys later."

©MGA

There weren't many people around as I tramped through the snow towards the ice rink. It was fun making fresh footprints in the crisp white powder. And the snowflakes that landed on my lashes gave me a fantastic idea for a frosty makeover! By the time I reached the rink my cheeks were glowing and I was feeling sorry for my friends - they were missing out on an awesome day, even though it was icy cold!

But after I had been on the ice for a few minutes, I was starting to change my mind. I really love skating and I have had a few lessons, but it wasn't nearly so much fun without Sasha doing her mad, daring spins, Jade whizzing around at top speed, and Cloe trying to do dramatic twirls, then losing her balance and falling over!

I decided to do a little practice and then head back to Cloe's for some hot chocolate by the fire. I skated a few figures on the ice and followed them with a couple of toe loops. I tried some camel spins and then finished up by skimming across the rink, skating backwards and forwards and tracing a spiral sequence on the ice..

96

©MGA

I did a final spiral, skating on one leg, then headed over to the exit, wishing my friends were there. But as I was about to step off the ice, I heard someone calling my name. I whirled around with a huge smile, thinking that the others had changed their minds, but instead I saw Dana waving at me from the other side of the rink. She was standing there with a group of girls I didn't know, and she beckoned to me to come across, so I skated over.

"Hi Dana!" I called as I came to a sharp stop next to her, spraying a little ice from my blades. "You risked the snow too, huh?"

"Nothing's gonna keep me away from the ice!" Dana said with a smile. "We're prepping for a big competition, so we just had to make it here to practise!"

I knew that Dana was an awesome skater and that she went in for a lot of competitions.

"Is this your skating team?" I asked.

"Pretty Princess, meet Maribel, Vinessa and Maylin. You guys, this is Yasmin."

Dana's friends were really sweet and soon we were all chatting as if we'd known each other for years!

©MGA

I was surprised
to see that Maylin had taken
her skates off.

"Maylin has hurt her knee," Dana explained,
looking really worried. "We're totally
panicked! She can't perform with a bad
knee - and we'll be disqualified without
the fourth member of our team!"

"We were about to give up, when
Dana saw you!" Maribel added,
with a fiery twinkle in her
eyes.

I swallowed hard.
"Me?"

"You're a stylin'
figure skater,"
said Dana
eagerly. "I know
you could help
us out. Please
say yes!"

How could I refuse?
"Of course I'll help you
out!" I agreed with a laugh.
"But I'm sure I'm nowhere near as
polished as you guys!"

"We'll show you our routine - you'll soon pick it
up!" cried Maribel, leaping out onto the ice. "I'll
show you my part first!"

Maribel was a super-skilled skater. Her
skating style was passionate and exciting!
I watched as she performed a super-
cool routine, full of complicated triple toe
loops and high jumps. When she finished I
applauded loudly.

"Not bad, right?" said Maribel, flashing me a grin as
she stopped next to me.

©MGA

Then Dana whizzed out onto the ice, polished and perfect. She was so laid back that she made her routine look easy, but I knew that it was full of complex steps, turns and loops. "That was cutting edge, Sugar Shoes!" I called, clapping.

It was Vinessa's turn next. I had already realised that she was a complete romantic, so it was no surprise that her skating style was soft and dreamy - poetry in motion! Her platinum-blonde hair flew out around her as she spun through her beautiful routine.

Gorgeous!" I said as I applauded her as well. "But what do I have to do?"

"You'll be doing your own individual routine just like us," said Dana. "Three of us repeat a spiral and step sequence while one of us performs our routine, then we all perform a final grand routine together...!"

"... which ends up with you on our shoulders," added Maribel.

"That takes perfect balance," Maylin told me.

"And we only have two days until the competition," Dana finished.

"So there's no pressure, then!" I exclaimed, hoping I wouldn't let them down.

"You have awesome balance, Pretty Princess," Maribel assured me. "You'll be totally cool!"

©MGA

I was super eager to get started! It would make a great insider exclusive on the world of figure skating for the school paper. Also, it wouldn't hurt to show the others what they had missed out on! It still bugged me that they hadn't come with me to the rink, and it would be pretty cool to win a trophy while they were still hanging around the house!

We got started straight away, practising the first part of the routine. Maylin sat by the side of the rink, ready to call out instructions if I forgot anything. After an hour and a half of solid practice, we decided to take a break and head over to the ice-rink café for some hot chocolate.

The ice-rink café was a super-stylin' zone to relax and take five after being on the ice, but the important thing to know is that they used specially frosted glass that meant you could only see through the glass one way. And that's what caused all the trouble!

©MGA

While I had been busy with the team on the ice, my best friends had started to feel guilty about not joining me. They had come all the way to the ice rink and they walked in just as I was giggling at one of Maribel's funny stories. I couldn't see them through the frosted glass - but they thought I was ignoring them!

Feeling hurt and angry, my friends left without saying hello... and I saw them as they walked out! I tried to call to them, but they seemed to be ignoring me. I felt terrible - did they think I was too busy with my new friends to care about them any more? I really wanted to chase after them, but the team was already getting up to start practising again. I couldn't let them down, so I could only watch sadly as Cloe, Sasha and Jade left the rink..

©MGA

101

All weekend, I was so busy practising with the ice-skating team that I didn't have a chance to see the others. I was at the rink as soon as it opened and I didn't leave until last thing at night - there was no time for anything except ice skating!

I was having lots of fun with my new friends! Maribel always had a great skating tip to share, Maylin was super-supportive and Vinessa made us all laugh by with her hilarious stories. But underneath it all I was really starting to miss my best girls. The competition was on Sunday night and I definitely didn't want to perform without them - we were **always there to support each other** in everything. They had to be there!

On Saturday night I managed to stay awake long enough to send my best girls an email, explaining how I was helping Dana's team out. I invited them to come and see me skate, hoping they would reply straight away. But no one was online, so I had to go to bed.

I checked my email before I left in the morning, but there was still no reply. I wasn't too worried though - they were probably still in bed!

©MGA

I kept breaking away from the team throughout the day to check my email on the computer at the ice rink. But each time it was the same story - 'No new messages'. My heart was sinking lower and lower - I knew I wouldn't do as well without them cheering me on!

When it was almost time for the competition , we got into our costumes and I went over my routine one final time. There were butterflies in my stomach and I really wished my best friends were there to calm me down. Still, I knew I had to try my best for my new friends. Our team was called and we stepped onto the ice. My heart was pounding, but I was determined to do everything I could to help my team.

I took a deep breath and looked out at the sea of faces in the audience. To my amazement, there in the front row were Cloe, Jade and Sasha! They were cheering and waving - they had come after all!

©MGA

As soon as I saw my best friends, all the butterflies disappeared! The music began and we glided into our routine. We spun and whirled around the rink as Maribel, Vinessa and Dana did their individual routines.

Then it was my turn! I put all my heart into it, trying to dazzle the judges with camel spins, toe loops and edge jumps. At last we all came together for the finale and I was hoisted high above the ice, all four of us spinning as if we were one person!

The music stopped and we bowed as the audience applauded and cheered. But the loudest applause came from my best friends in the front row! Sasha threw red roses at our feet and Jade gave a piercing whistle as we skated off the ice!

My friends rushed around the rink and crowded around me for a big group hug.
"I'm sorry I haven't called you - I've been so busy training!" I cried.
"We're sorry that we didn't just come and find you!" replied Cloe.
"You guys have got to meet my team mates!" I said, pulling my new friends into the hug too. Maylin limped up to us and joined in as well, grinning from ear to ear.

©MGA

"You guys were totally awesome!" Sasha gasped.
"That jump you did - incredible!" Cloe told Maribel.
"You were all fantastic!" Jade agreed.
"I'm worried that the judges will pick up on how new I am," I said.
"No way, girl, you skated like a pro!" Dana assured me.

I wanted to believe Dana, but I was nervous. Could I really have skated well enough to satisfy the eagle-eyed judges?

Just then the judge began to announce the results. We didn't win the bronze medal. We didn't win the silver medal. I sighed... had I let my new friends down after all?

"... and finally!" bellowed the judge, "the gold medal is awarded to - Dana, Maribel, Vinessa & Yasmin!"
I could hardly believe it! We went up to collect the medals and then I dashed back to my friends to show mine to them.
"That's totally cool," said Jade, holding up the medal so that it caught the light and glinted off the ice.
"It's cool, but it's not the best prize," I said. "The best prize is having my best friends right here to share it with me!"

©MGA

Winter Wonderland

Some people hate winter – but my theory is that you just have to know how to make it fun! Check out some of the ways we make winter a happenin' season!

winter blues

Everyone knows that fresh vegetables are good for your health - but did you know that they're good for your happiness too? Whenever the winter blues attack, cook up a platter of colourful vegetables, from bright green asparagus and broccoli to mashed parsnips and sweet potatoes. You'll soon start to feel better!

winter parties

Nothing is gonna cheer you up as much as holding a dazzlin' winter party! Plan carefully and think about everything that makes a party smooth and spectacular - from the invitations to the decorations!

Why not pick 'winter wonderland' as your party theme and decorate with silver sparkles, glitter and foil 'icicles'?

winter fashions

- A new season - a new wardrobe! Hit the mall and check out all the latest and greatest styles!

- Keep up with the winter catwalk fashions. Why not arrange to have your fave fashion mag delivered straight to your door?

- Invest in a really well-cut winter coat in a classic style. Even though they are quite expensive, some styles are always in vogue, and a good coat will last for several years to come!

- You spend a lot of time wrapped up warm during winter, which means that you don't always get to show off your fabulous fashions! So think accessories - gorgeous earrings and dazzlin' necklaces will always be attention grabbers! And don't forget a totally cute scarf!

106

©MGA

winter friends

Organise a movie night with your best girls. You'll need a few delicious desserts and some yummy hot drinks. Grab armfuls of soft blankets, comfy cushions and fluffy pillows to turn the floor into a huge bed, then snuggle up and put a romantic comedy on the DVD player!

winter fun

So it's way too cold to go to the park or to hang out on the beach - that doesn't mean you've got nowhere to go!

- Ice rink - grab your best friends and persuade them to take ice skating lessons with you! It'll keep you fit and you will have tons of fun - as well as learning how to move with elegance and style!

- Bowling alley - get some teams together and hit the lanes for some seriously fun competitions!

- The cinema - it's a total entertainment package! Make a regular date with your friends to check out the latest releases!

winter beauty

During winter, you need to put your beauty regime on red alert! Your skin and hair can get battered by the chilly weather and biting winds, so make sure you look after yourself. If you take the time to pamper yourself, when summer comes around your skin will be ready to tan and your hair will be silky and bouncy!

- Moisturise every day.

- Use lip balm to keep your pout smooth and supple.

- Use a deep hair-conditioning treatment once a week.

- When you step out of the bath, rub baby oil into your skin to seal in moisture.

- Wear a hat to stay warm and protect your hair from harsh winds.

- Manicure your nails once a week and use clear nail varnish to protect them.

- Get regular exercise in the pool or at the gym.

- Wear pure-wool gloves - cold weather can make your nails brittle and your skin dry.

- If you always get cold hands, invest in some instant warmers and carry them in your pockets.

- Keep drinking lots of water - this will help your skin to look glowing even in the dead of winter!

End the Year

This has been one of our all-time fave years! We've made tons of new friends, had plenty of adventures and taken some awesome snaps! Have a look through our memories of the year — and add a few of your own, too!

Stick a photo of you and your best friends here, and describe when and why it was taken!

©MGA

POPular

Check out my top look for school this year - mix 'n' match fun! Everyone thought my cute lil pink bows were super sweet! Cloe x

DRAMA Queen

My biggest crush was

....

The best day of the year was

....

My top fashion find was

....

My fave class was

....

My fave teacher was

....

One of my fave nights out was also my most embarrassing night out! We were watching a scary film at the cinema and I was so totally into it that when Jade tapped me on the shoulder, I jumped into the air and screamed! My popcorn landed all over the guy in front - I was totally blushin'! But we had so much fun - a perfect example of an awesome girls' night out!

I'm lovin'... fruit-flavoured lip gloss
The next big trend will be... totally blinged-out looks!

with Attitude!

2 good
+ 2 be
4 gott
cause i
4 ever
ROCKS!

©MGA

©MGA

Princess

This is my definition of fashion flair! Using your school tie as a belt is so retro cool! Sasha X

The next big trend will be... goin' mod in black & white - totally back to basics!

I'm lovin'... crisp white shirts with denim jeans and long boots

GIRL POWER

My fave styles this year have been a mixture of old school and new funk - I get such a buzz from hitting the malls and tracking down the hottest new threads!

Jade snapped this pic as we were walking to school for our first day back after the holiday? What an awesome start to the term? Yasmin x

My fave class this year was creative writing - surprise surprise? I always get inspired by the totally creative atmosphere and I leave the class buzzing with fantastic ideas?

The next big trend will be... colours pulled from nature - gorgeous flowery hues and soft leafy greens?

I'm lovin'... wrap-around tops in soft, silky fabrics

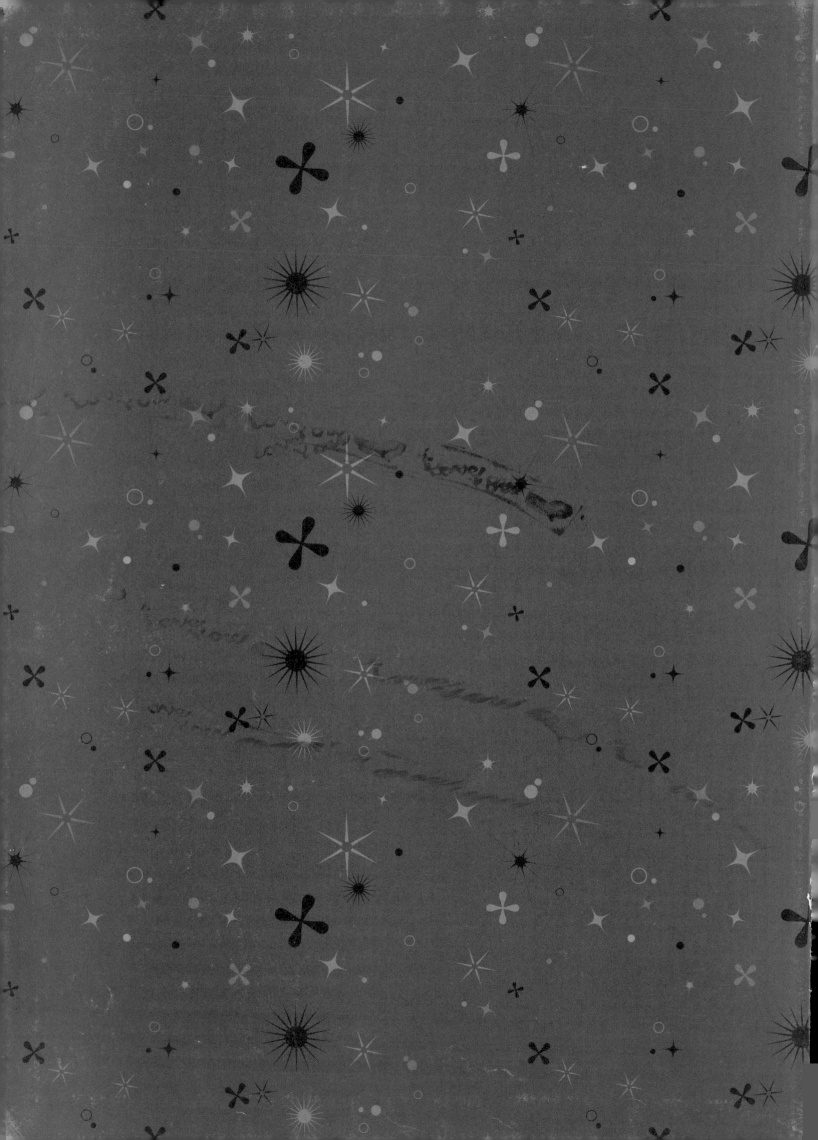